THE
WEATHER BOOK

FOR PRIMARY TEACHERS

STEVE HARRISON

SENIOR ADVISER

LANCASHIRE EDUCATION AUTHORITY

FRANK HAVARD

DEPUTY HEADTEACHER

HOLLINS SCHOOL, ACCRINGTON

SIMON & SCHUSTER
EDUCATION

Text© Steve Harrison and Frank Havard 1991
Design and artwork© Simon & Schuster Ltd 1991
Photographs© The sources credited

First published in 1991 in Great Britain by
Simon & Schuster Education
Wolsey House, Wolsey Road
Hemel Hempstead HP2 4SS

Printed in Great Britain by
BPCC Hazell Books
Paulton and Aylesbury

A catalogue record of this book is available
from the British Library

ISBN 0 7501 0124 5

Edited by John Day
Designed by Jane Hannath
Artwork by Peter Beard/King Ink (page 3), Robert & Rhoda
Burns (page 79), Kay Dixey/Gisèle Kearley (pages 62, 63)
Anna Hancock (pages 14-19), Jane Hannath (pages 10,
11, 24, 25, 28-32, 34-37, 39, 40, 48, 53, 54, 56-58, 64-69,
73-76), Brian Hoskin/Simon Girling (pages 4-9, 12, 13,
20-23, 26, 27, 33, 38, 49-52, 55, 59-61, 72, 77), Jenny
Press/Simon Girling (pages 44, 55), Michael Salter/Simon
Girling (pages 41-43), Joanna Williams/Gisèle Kearley
(pages 46, 47)

Cover artwork by Liz Black and Jane Hannath

Typeset by Kelvin Meadows/Kingsway Advertising

Photo research by Caroline Smith

Photo credits
The authors and publisher thank the following for their
kind permission to reproduce their photographs: Science
Photo Library (pages 70,71), Unilab Ltd (page 50, right).
All the other photographs are the property of the
authors.

Other acknowledgements
The authors and publisher thank the following for their
kind permission to reproduce the poems on page 42 to 45.

Curtis Brown/Ogden Nash, 'Winter Morning', from
Collected Poems of Ogden Nash (Dent).
Exley Publications Ltd/Father Gander, 'Twinkle, Twinkle
Little Star', from Father Gander Nursery Rhymes.
Jean Kenward, 'Sir Winter'.
Pan Macmillan Ltd/Vernon Scannell, 'The Death of a
Snowman', from Allsorts 2 (Macmillan).
Penguin Ltd/Kit Wright, 'It's Winter, it's Winter', from
Hot Dog and Other Poems (Kestrel).
Random Century Group/Roger McGough, 'The Fight of
the Year', from Watchwords (Cape); Shel Silverstein,
'Rain', from Where the Sidewalk Ends (Cape).

They also warmly thank the following for their generous
help: A&L Scientific, Meteorological Office, Moor Park
Observatory, Seed Sports, Unilab, and the staff and
children of Peel Park County Primary School, Sherwood
County Primary School and Stonefold CE School.

INTRODUCTION

WIND

Sensing the wind 4
Strong winds 5
Controlling the wind 6-7
Windblown 8
Wind direction 9
Which direction? 10
Windmill template 11
Wind speed 12
Wind effects 13

RAIN

Sensing the rain 14
Types of rain 15
Effects of rain 16
Coping with rain 17
Where does the water go? 18
How much rain? 19

TEMPERATURE

Cold and hot weather 20
Temperature changes 21
How does it feel? 22-23
Keeping warm 24
Keeping warm, staying cool 25
Ice cold 26
Investigating cold 27
What can we do? 28
How hot is it? 29
Air temperatures 30
Ups and downs 31-32

WEATHER PATTERNS

Weather recording 33
Stepping out 34
Weather symbols 35
Clothes 36
Today is . . . 37
Looking up 38
Cloud cover 39
Weekly weather record 40

LANGUAGE

Language 41-45

INFORMATION TECHNOLOGY

Information technology 46-47
Concept Keyboard overlay 48
Concept Keyboard 49
More information technology 50

HUMIDITY

Humidity 51
Humidity and nature 52
How humid? 53
Rising damp 54

ELECTRICAL ACTIVITY

Thunder and lightning 55
Making electrical charges 56-57

PRESSURE

Pressure at work 58
Pressure the predictor 59

RAIN

The water cycle 60
'Mineral' water 61

WIND

Wind speed 62
Wind direction 63
The Beaufort scale 64
Recording direction 65

WEATHER PATTERNS

Connect and compare 66
Weather connections 67
Comparing weather 68
British Isles master map 69
Satellite pictures of UK 70-71

ECONOMICS AND CLIMATE

Economic and industrial
understanding 72
Accidents and the weather 73
Power to the people 74
Send out the gritters 75-76
Climate and people 77

AT Cross-reference 78
Resources and sources 79
Index 80

We seek to meet a number of objectives:

- To recognise the long tradition of teaching about the weather in the primary years and to build on current best practice.
- To give non-specialist teachers a sound knowledge base from which to teach weather studies.
- To provide a variety of exciting classroom activities which will enhance children's understanding of weather.
- To supply supporting material in the form of resources and activity sheets which children can use individually and in groups for focused work.
- To identify the potential for the IT dimension and develop it more systematically.
- To draw together the contributions of a whole range of curricular subjects and themes to the study of weather. Geography, science, English, technology, maths and cross-curricular themes are featured.

Teaching about the weather

Weather work should not be a self-contained, isolated study but should relate to other aspects of the curriculum. In geography, for example, a study of your own locality or region should include a study of its weather. To a large extent, the weather influences local industry, farming, settlement patterns, leisure provision and tourism. In studying the dominance of particular crops in local agriculture, you should also study the weather conditions which affect or even determine the decision to grow them.

Any study of contrasting UK localities, localities in the economically developing world and in the EC should include similarities and differences with all aspects of your own locality, including the weather. Work on, for example, experiments, model-making, data processing, poetry, can then underpin the local study. This is what primary schools can do and should do. They have the flexibility of time and the advantage of one teacher helping children make genuine rigorous connections. Done well, there is no better way for children to learn (or for teachers to teach).

Some of the activities and experiments suggested will be new to many primary school teachers. However, all have been tried and tested with primary school children.

Using this book

Broadly, the first half of the book covers work more appropriate to Key Stage 1, and the second half to Key Stage 2. However, the book is not formally divided into two sections because children do not learn in Key Stages. Certain themes are introduced in the early pages and revisited later in the book. This is intended to help schools plan for continuity and progression. Teachers will need to decide what experiences and activities are to be covered when, and to build these into school policy and practice. The language section (pages 41-45) provides material for the whole primary age range, as does the IT section (pages 46-50).

To help teaching the National Curriculum, the matrix on page 78 cross-refers the 'weather' Statements of Attainment in geography and science to pages in this book.

Activity Sheets

Activity Sheets, identified by A in the Contents, are photocopiable and contain assignments for children. The exception is the map of the British Isles (Gall's projection as specified in the National Curriculum) on page 69 – a blank outline which can be used by children in many ways: for example, to show mean seasonal patterns for rainfall and temperature, to show weather forecasts, to depict weather systems and to display school links in a weather data network.

In addition, there are 'resource' pages, such as 6, 13, 14 and 20, which contain 'talk about' materials. These may also be photocopied according to individual teacher's needs.

Can we feel the wind?

On our face

Does it feel dry?
The wind evaporates
moisture from our skin.

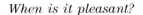

In our hair

If we face the wind, which
way does our hair move?

What happens if we turn
our back to the wind?

When is it pleasant?

When is it unpleasant?

Children have an incidental knowledge and experience of the wind through their everyday lives. We need to encourage them to look more closely for signs of the great variety of effects which come under the broad heading of 'wind' – from breeze to gale. Exploring the effects of the wind, talking about the wind, sharing poems and stories about the wind will help to raise the children's general awareness of the natural world about them.

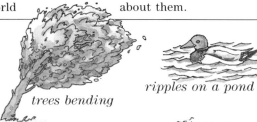

trees bending

ripples on a pond

Can we see the wind?

litter blowing

smoke blowing sideways

Make a mobile and hang it outside or by an open window.

Who has seen the wind?
Neither you nor I,
But when the trees bow down their heads
The wind is passing by.

Christina Rossetti

Can we hear the wind?

bottles falling and rolling

leaves rustling

chimes

doors slam

We hear its effects and sometimes the rushing of air.

Depicting the wind

mime   *drama*   *dance*

painting

music

Wind effects

Use photographs and other pictures to encourage discussion.

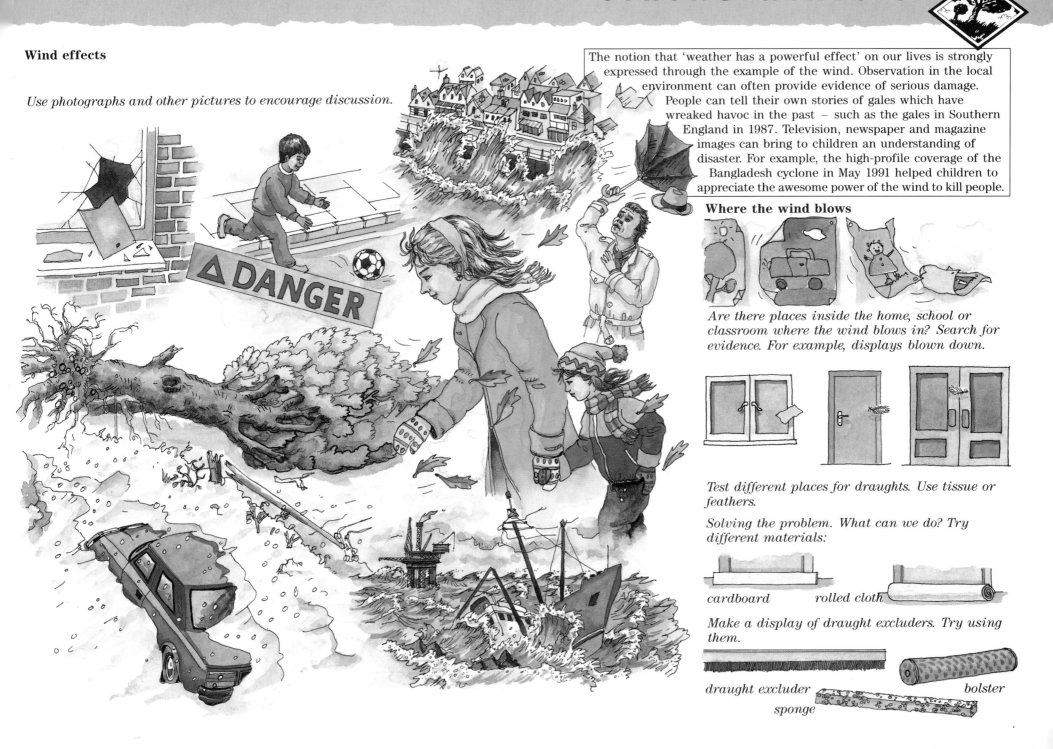

The notion that 'weather has a powerful effect' on our lives is strongly expressed through the example of the wind. Observation in the local environment can often provide evidence of serious damage. People can tell their own stories of gales which have wreaked havoc in the past – such as the gales in Southern England in 1987. Television, newspaper and magazine images can bring to children an understanding of disaster. For example, the high-profile coverage of the Bangladesh cyclone in May 1991 helped children to appreciate the awesome power of the wind to kill people.

Where the wind blows

Are there places inside the home, school or classroom where the wind blows in? Search for evidence. For example, displays blown down.

Test different places for draughts. Use tissue or feathers.

Solving the problem. What can we do? Try different materials:

cardboard   rolled cloth

Make a display of draught excluders. Try using them.

draught excluder
sponge
bolster

The legends of the heroes of Ancient Greece are vivid and lend themselves to drama and other creative work with children at Key Stage 1. An example is the story of Odysseus and the bag of winds, taken from Homer's Odyssey.

Odysseus and his men had blinded the one-eyed giant Polyphemus and escaped to the island of Aeolus. Aeolus was the master of the winds. He took pity on Odysseus and collected together all the world's winds except for the wind which would blow Odysseus's ship back to the island of Ithaca. Aeolus put all the other winds in a bag, which he gave to Odysseus.

As his ship sailed gently towards Ithaca, Odysseus fell asleep. He had not told his men what was in the bag. They were curious and began to talk among themselves – perhaps there was gold and silver treasure in the bag. They could no longer bear not knowing – they opened the bag!

All the world's winds were released at once. A mighty storm blew the ship this way and that – far, far from home – to seas they had never visited before and to an island full of cannibals.

Can we capture the wind and use it later?

Make a wind

Make a fan

Draw a design

Fasten one end (staple, paper clip or glue)

Mark and fold every 3 cm

Match picture to function

Ask the children to choose an item and paint or draw a picture of the job it does.

OR

Write about the job done.

Object	Job it does
	dries clothes

Electric wind power

Cut out pictures of electrical appliances from old mail-order catalogues.

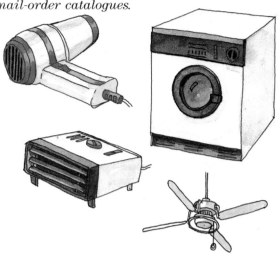

Sort them into those that

make wind

don't make wind

or those that blow

hot air   both   cold air

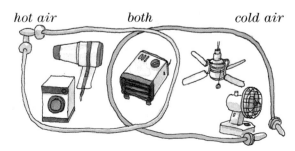

The wind dries our clothes

Which dries faster?

a windy spot

a spot where the air is still

To make the test fair, the only variable should be the wind. Therefore make sure

- *The lengths of washing line are the same.*
- *The two items are the same: for example, handkerchiefs.*
- *They are both in the sun or both in the shade.*
- *Both are immersed in water for the same length of time.*

The scarecrow's best friend

A scarecrow has loose, ragged clothes so that they flap vigorously in the wind.

Design and build a scarecrow.

Which materials will blow best in the wind?

Design and make other bird scarers which use the wind.

pegs, string and bottle tops

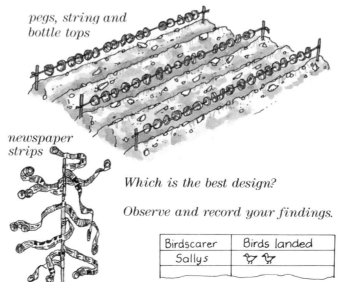

newspaper strips

Which is the best design?

Observe and record your findings.

Birdscarer	Birds landed
Sallys	🐦 🐦

Stick a bird on the chart every time one is seen landing.

Seeds in the wind

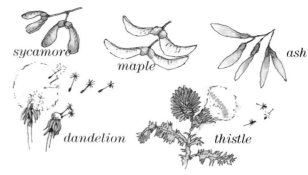

sycamore *maple* *ash*

dandelion *thistle*

Examine seeds at close hand.

Make a collection of different seeds. Which shape travels the best? Test them on a windy day.

Which direction?

The detailed recording of wind direction and speed is dealt with on pages 62-65.

At this stage, we are seeking only to encourage children's awareness that the wind's direction can be observed and recorded.

Once children are confident with four compass points, they should move on to eight.

Throw grass in the air.

Face the wind.

Hold a wet finger in the air.

The classroom-made wind vane must have a greater surface area at its tail. This will be 'pushed' by the wind so the 'point' faces in the direction from which the wind is blowing.

Tie a ribbon to a stick.

Allow a sponge ball to roll.

Which way is the wind blowing?

Observe where leaves have fallen.

Make a windmill to test direction.

Make a wind vane.

Use two pieces of card glued to a pen top.

Observe wind vanes.

Use the Activity Sheet on page 10 to record 'leaf' data. This provides opportunities to reinforce the fact that a wind is named according to the direction from which it blows. Many children take time to internalise this.

Each of the activities on this page should be accompanied by a discussion of wind direction.

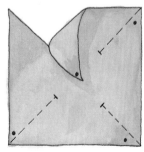
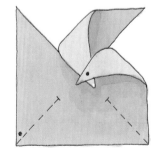
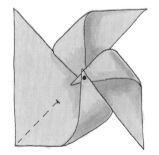
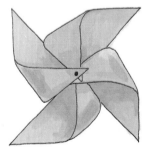

WHICH DIRECTION?

Which direction is the wind blowing from?

Find a tree and clear away all the leaves under it.

Using a compass, mark on the ground North, East, South and West.

Everyday, collect the leaves which have blown off and mark on the map where they landed. Use a different colour crayon each day. Count the leaves.

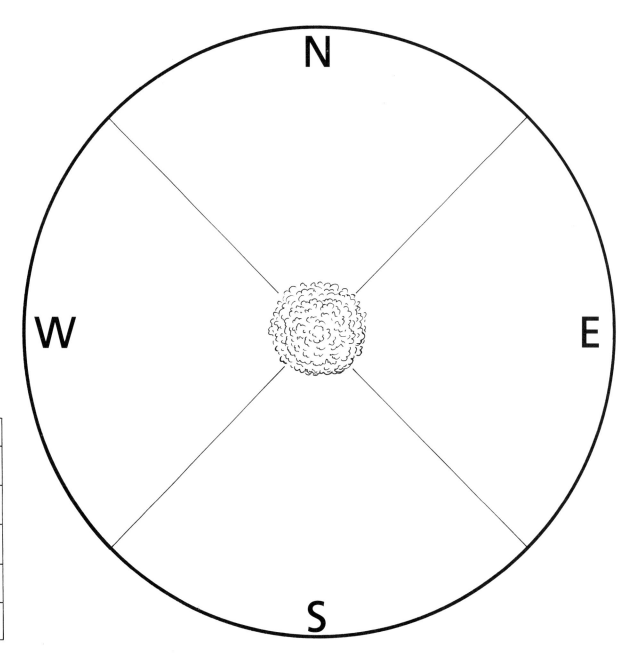

Keep a record for a week.

Day	Number of leaves	Direction wind blowing from

Remember If, for example, you find the leaves to the **East** of the tree, the wind is blowing from the **West**.

Photocopy this plan on thin card, but paper will do. Cut along the broken lines. Make small holes at the circles. Fold the windmill as shown on page 9, threading it on to a drinking straw. Cut the straw to a length of 1 cm and slide it on to a nail. A bead on each side of the straw 'axle' will help free running. Push the nail into a balsawood stick.

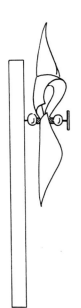

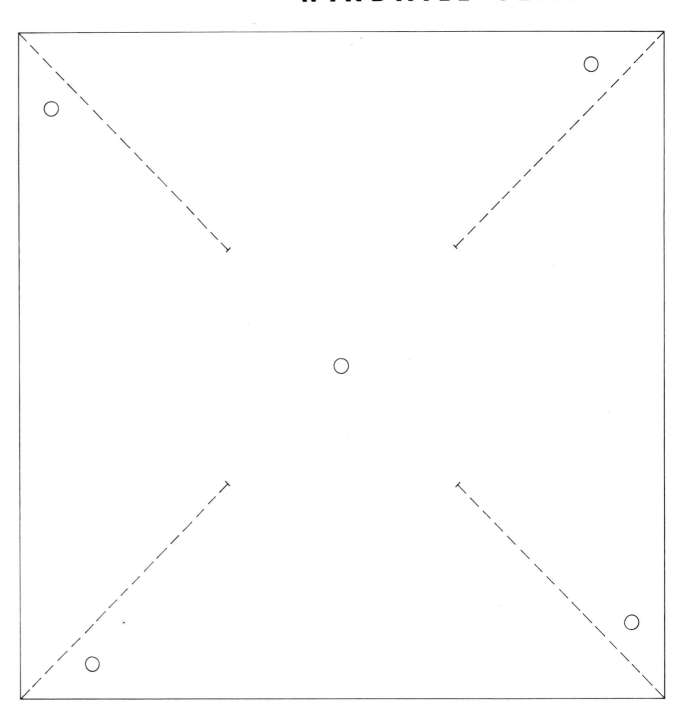

How fast does the windmill turn?

*Colour one of the segments.
Working in pairs, count
the number of turns
in a certain time.
Use a stop clock.*

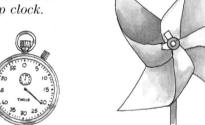

Record your findings.

Day	Turns per minute
Mon	
Tues	
Weds	
Thurs	
Fri	

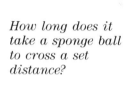

*How long does it
take a sponge ball
to cross a set
distance?*

Keep a weekly record.

Day	Time taken
Mon	10 seconds

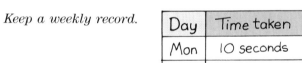

Make a boat.

How long to cross the water?

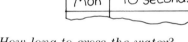

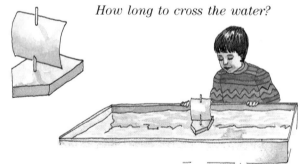

Is it still?   Does it bend?   Does it touch me?

Classification of wind speeds

*Detailed wind-speed measurement using standard units is covered on page 62.
With younger children, the concern should be broad categories of wind speed and
arbitrary measurements. The emphasis is on developing tests for wind speed
which are logical and include gradation. The children should have a whole range
of materials available for their exploratory investigations.*

*Build a paper cup tower.
Observe it in the wind.
How many cups stay in place?
three stay = still
two stay = slow
one stays = fast
none stays = strong*

*Try using different
materials to classify
wind speeds.*

For example:

1	tissue	still
2	newspaper	slow
3	card	fast
4	wood	strong

Signs of rain

Can nature tell us when it is going to rain?

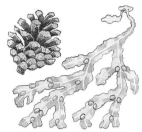

These are sensitive to the amount of water vapour in air. Damp air causes a cone to close tightly and seaweed to become limp and rubbery.

Ask the children to test the accuracy of these to forecast rain. Record their results over a week.

Day	Cone	Forecast	Actual weather
Monday	Open	Dry	Fine
Tuesday			

Take a close look

Collect a few snowflakes, hailstones, or raindrops on a plastic or metal tray. Examine them closely using a magnifying glass or Midispector.

What is precipitation?

This is the general name for all types of moisture falling from clouds: rain, sleet, snow and hail.

Are snow and rain the same?

Fill a jar with snow and take it indoors. Allow the snow to melt. Discover the relationship between the depth of the snow in the jar and the amount of water when the snow has melted. How many jars would we need to measure to make a fair test?

Can we see the moisture in the air?

Music, dance and drama

Play a musical 'picture' of the rain: for example, 'The Rising Storm'. Use tambourines, shakers, bells, classroom-made percussion instruments.

Make costumes using crepe paper.

Tell the story of Noah (Genesis, Chapters 6-8).

Make a large freize as background to the ark. Change the role-play corner into an ark. Act out the story.

Sing 'The Animals Went in Two by Two' or 'Noah Once He Built the Ark'.

Flooding

Re-enact the story of Noah using the water trough. Use watering cans, sieves, or punctured plastic bottles to make 'rain'. The children place boats and other models in the empty trough and then 'rain' on them.

Welcome rain

Harnessing the rain

Where does drinking water come from?

Do farmers have enough/too much rain?

Sand play

Children can try moving water by using channels and mounds. (Irrigation and dykes.)

Make a rainbow

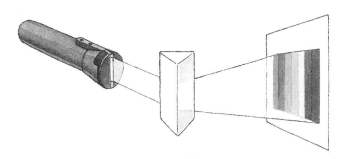

In a darkened area, the children shine the narrow beam of light through the prism to produce the colours of the rainbow: red, orange, yellow, green blue, indigo, violet.

All these colours have come from the white light. Each colour merges with its adjacent colours. Indigo and violet merge as purple and are difficult to see as separate colours.

A raindrop acts like a prism and splits up the sunlight.

Sing 'I Can Sing a Rainbow'.

Dr Foster went to Gloucester
In a shower of rain.
He stepped in a puddle,
Right up to his middle
And never went there again.

What do we wear?

Make a fine/wet weather collage. Start by drawing around a child in the class.

fine weather   *wet weather*

Make a weekly record.

Day	Weather	Coats worn	Wellingtons	Hats
Monday	wet	32	10	15
Tuesday				

Why do we wear special clothes?

Test materials to find out which are waterproof.

Place different materials over a bowl and drip water from a pipette over each material. How many drips before the water goes through? Use garments from the dressing-up box.

Test materials for use in an umbrella. Use small samples stretched over a container and fastened with an elastic band.

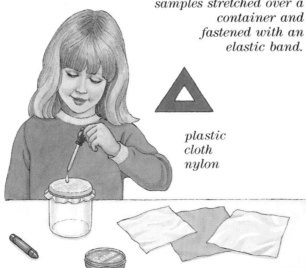

*plastic
cloth
nylon*

Can you make the material waterproof. Use wax crayons, polish. Be careful with domestic chemicals.

Keeping dry at home

Can you make a waterproof roof for your model house?

Which shape of roof is most effective?

keeping dry

Make a collage using old mail-order catalogues.

Polishing shoes

Drop the same amount of water on each shoe. Observe with a magnifying glass. Feel inside.

Poem with actions

Incey Wincey Spider
Climbing up the spout;
Down came the rain
And washed the spider out.
Out came the sun
And dried up all the rain;
Incey Wincey Spider
Climbing up again.

Anon

Running water

What happens if
we drop water
on to the plastic?
Put more blocks
under one end.

Try card – with and
without polish on it.

Where does the
water from
the roof go?

Look around
the outside
of your
school.

*Make a fair test to find out
where water goes.*

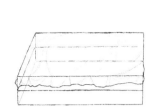

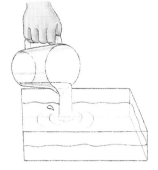

Use the same amount of water in both trays.
Cover one tray with cling film. Leave both trays
outside in the sunshine. Has any water escaped?
Can you see how it might get out? The cling film
traps the evaporating water.

Watering the ground

Pour water on to different types of ground: soil,
grass, sand, stone, tarmac. Where does the water
go?

Use chalk to draw around a small puddle in the
playground. It is best to 'make' a puddle on a
dry, sunny day. What happens?

Finding shelter

Where is it driest?

Sometimes the water (in the form of snow) stays
on a surface and builds up.

How much rain has fallen?

You will be surprised (and disappointed) at the amount of rain which falls, even in a heavy downpour. Use a variety of collecting containers.

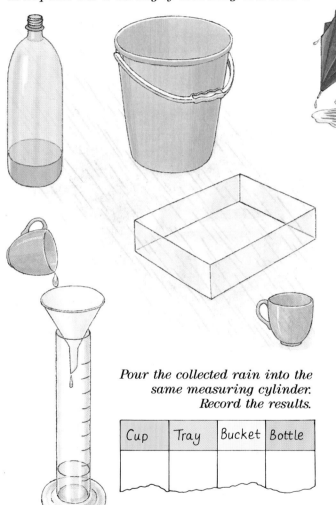

Pour the collected rain into the same measuring cylinder. Record the results.

Cup	Tray	Bucket	Bottle

Which container collected the most rain. Why? (The greater the surface area of the opening, the more will be collected.)

Fair testing

Use the same collecting device each day. Children working at Level 1 could use a bucket to collect the rain. Pour it into small screw-top bottles in which a few drops of food colouring have been placed. Record your findings for a week.

Measure the amount of water by non-standard units (such as fingers) or standard units (such as millimetres).

Compare the results. Which day had the most rainfall?

Put the bottles side by side to compare the different water levels.

Interpret the data. On which day did you not need an umbrella?

A week's rainfall

Mon	Tues	Wed	Thurs	Fri

Children working at Levels 2 and 3 may wish to design their own rain collector.

A simple and effective rain collector can be made from a clear plastic bottle.

Secure the collector by sinking it in a hole in the ground, or by surrounding it with bricks. A gauge (plastic ruler) may be taped to the collector for direct measurement. The curved base will give inaccurate readings, so make a starting point. Fill the collector to it each day. (If the bottle has a black base, the top of this could be used as the starting point.) Food colouring will help visibility.

Day	Rainfall	Symbol
Monday	2 mm	
Tuesday	0 mm	

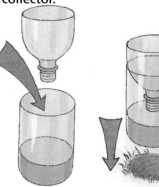

The amount of rain falling is the depth measured. The area of the open top is irrelevant but the container must have a consistent cross-section, such as a right cylinder.

Record your findings.

What happens to the temperature at night?

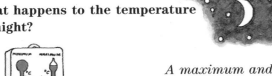

A maximum and minimum thermometer will 'save' the highest and lowest temperatures until it is reset.

Record the children's findings over a week. Reset the thermometer each day.

Day	During the day		Overnight	
	maximum	minimum	maximum	minimum
Monday				
Tuesday				

The children should be encouraged to look for patterns in the weekly record. They should also comment on how they felt in the night – did it seem warm or cold? Encourage the children to predict what the minimum and maximum temperatures might be, relating them to how warm or cold they felt the night before.

Observation of the sky before going to bed and when rising can be recorded.

Day	Sky	Temp
Mon	clear	
Tues	patchy cloud	
Wed	full cloud cover	

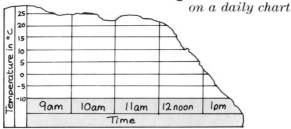

Cloud can act as a large blanket at night, preventing the upward loss of warm air.

Does the temperature change through the day?

Record the temperature through the day every hour from 09:00 to 16:00:

Day _ _ _ _ _ Month _ _ _ _ _ _ _	
Time	Temperature
🕘 9am	
🕙 10am	

on a daily chart

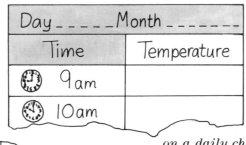

as a graph

or on a weekly chart

Time of reading	Day			
	Mon	Tues	Wed	Thurs
9.00am				
10.00am				

Compare each day's change in temperature. Save the data and compare winter/summer day changes.

Safety in cold weather

In cold weather, we wrap ourselves up in warm clothing. We take special care to protect our hands, feet and head.

Ice slides are fun for young children, but icy conditions are very hazardous for the elderly.

Solving a safety problem

How can we make pavements and steps safe for everyone?

Place the same number of ice cubes in two identical trays. Sprinkle table salt generously over the ice cubes on one tray only.

Observe over several minutes.

> The salt-covered ice cubes will melt first. Salt water freezes at a low temperature and will remain unfrozen at temperatures below 0°C (the freezing point of pure water).

How is the test kept fair?

When de-icing roads and pavements, grit or sand is mixed with the salt.

Take three bowls and fill one with water and ice cubes (1) another with warm water (2) and the third with hot water – not too hot (3).

Keep your hands in for 1 minute.

How does your left hand feel?
How does your right hand feel?

Then put both hands into the middle bowl at the same time.

How does your left hand feel?
How does your right hand feel?

Use a thermometer to measure the temperature of each bowl. Record your results.

Temperature		
Bowl 1	Bowl 2	Bowl 3

Is your hand a good thermometer?

Repeat the test with several bowls of water at different temperatures.

Estimate by feel first. Then measure accurately with a thermometer.

Record your results.

Temperature		
Bowl	Estimate	Measured
1		
2		
3		
4		
5		

Do your estimation skills improve (become more accurate) with practice?

How is your school?

How cold/hot are the classroom and the playground?

Record your results. Estimate first.

This could be done each day or it could be

Temperature inside the classroom		
Day	Estimate	Measured
Monday		

recorded at different times in one day.

Temperature outside	Tuesday 15th May	
Time	Estimate	Measured
9.00am		
10.00am		
11.00am		

Explore the differences between shade and sun.

Temperature		
Time	Sun	Shade

Find the hottest/coldest part of the classroom. What happens in the classroom if doors and windows are left open?

Classroom activities related to temperature, and experiments on keeping warm and staying cool need to be linked to seasonal patterns throughout the year. Children should be encouraged to think back to last summer or winter.

What did they wear? *What did they see?*
Where did they go? *What did they do?*

Recollections of other seasons can be compared directly with observations of the present season.

Season	Month	Temp	Feels
Winter	January	5°C	Cold

Season	Month	Temp	Feels
Summer	June	29°C	Hot

Keep records to compare.
Keep children's paintings, collages and other work.
Display winter alongside summer.

Using the photocopiable Activity Sheets

Cold and hot weather (page 20)

Discuss the winter scene. The earth at 'rest'.

Cold inhibits plant growth, therefore there is little for animals to eat. The way to survive is for animals to rest. Using as little energy as possible, the hibernating creature can last until the spring when temperatures will rise and the food supply becomes plentiful again.
Discuss the summer scene.
The temperatures facilitate plant growth, which in turn provides food for wildlife, farm animals and people.

Questions related to what the child is wearing in both scenes could lead to drawing on children's personal experience of wearing different clothes when visiting other countries.

winter sweater   *summer T-shirt*

Keeping warm (page 24)

You will need
two identical opened cans   large jug   two thermometers
timer   warm water   winter clothes

No sharp edges on cans
No mercury-filled thermometers
Warm water (not too hot!)

Making the test fair:
stirred water from same jug,
same amount of water in each can,
cans in same surroundings,
readings taken after
same length of time.

Variable: one tin is wrapped in warm clothing. If outside, place a scarf under the wrapped tin.

Repeat the test with different items of clothing.

Temperature	bare can	cans wrapped			
		mitten	scarf	hat	jumper

The test should be done outside on a cold day.

Dress two hot water bottles.

Record the fall in temperature.

Experiment using a number of layers. Does it make a difference?

Keeping warm, staying cool (page 25)

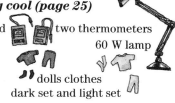
You will need
two identical dolls   two thermometers   60 W lamp
doll in metal foil   dolls clothes dark set and light set

The lamp must be controlled by an adult. It must be electrically safe and suitable for school use. Do not carry out this activity near water. No wet hands.

Organising the activity

Compare the colour of clothing worn by the children, especially indoor and outdoor clothing.
Do we wear different colours of clothes in winter from those in summer?

Dress one doll in light clothes, the other in dark. The children should record this pictorially. Place the thermometers so that the sensors (bulb or probes) are under the clothes in the chest region. Place the dolls side by side and place the lamp 20 cm centrally above the dolls.

Record the starting temperature. Switch on the lamp and record the temperature every minute.

Questions *Why does the temperature rise? Do the dolls feel different? (Adult supervision near lamp.)*

The lamp, like the sun, radiates heat energy. Dark, dull clothes absorb the heat better than light shiny ones, which reflect light.

Developments *On a hot day, use the sun instead of a lamp. Use cut-out dolls and cardboard clothes. Colour them with crayons – dark and light.*

A range of colours and/or textures may be tested. Research types and colour of people's clothing from different climates. Does their choice of clothing relate to your experiments? Design clothes for hot and cold climates. Think about colour and fabric.

KEEPING WARM

1

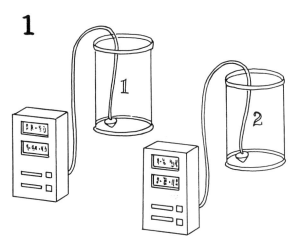

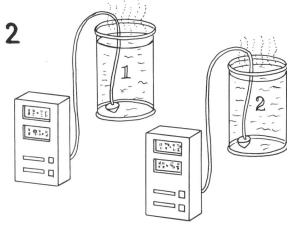

2

3

4

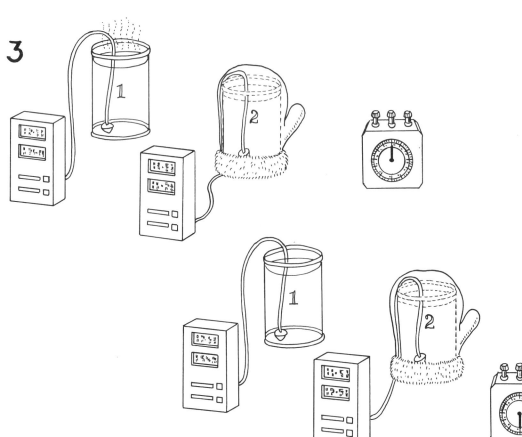

Time	Temperature of Can 1	Temperature of Can 2
Start		
Finish		

Minutes	Temperature	
	Doll A	Doll B
0		
1		
2		
3		
4		
5		

How cold is cold?

Crush some ice cubes. The easiest way to do this is to wrap the cubes in a tea towel and smash them with a wooden block.

Minutes	Temp	✓When ice melts
At start		
After 1		
2		
3		

Put the crushed ice in a rain gauge. Record the temperature every minute. At what temperature does water drip through to the lower container?

ICE MELTS AT 0° CELSIUS. WATER FREEZES AT 0° CELSIUS.

Examine ice cubes with a magnifying glass.

In what ways do they look different?

Ice balls

Large ice balls can be used for a variety of investigations. Fill several balloons with water to the size of a tennis ball. Knot them and place them in a plastic carrier bag (no holes) and then into a freezer overnight.

Peel off the balloon covering and examine the ice ball using a magnifying glass.

Can you see a yellow spot?

Are there any bubbles?

Place an ice ball in the scale pan. Observe and record what happens.

How does the ice ball feel?

What will happen to the weight as the ice melts?

How much of the iceball is above/below the water?

Is ice heavier than water?

Does it float?

What do these investigations reveal about icebergs and their danger to ships?

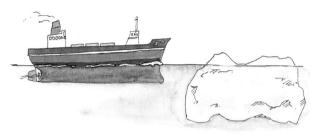

How is salt water different?

Dissolve half a cup of salt in a bowlful of water.

Does the ice ball float higher in salt water than in pure water? Add more salt to see what happens. Use fresh ice balls.

IMPURE WATER FREEZES AT A LOWER TEMPERATURE THAN PURE WATER.

The effects of freezing

What can you see when you breathe out through your mouth?

How does it feel to breathe in deeply through your nose?

Which parts of our bodies feel coldest? Ears, nose, fingers? Why? Do we feel as cold when we jump or run about?

Will it be ice right through? Is there anything under the ice?

What sounds do our feet make on frost-covered grass? What does it look/feel like?

USING THE PHOTOCOPIABLE ACTIVITY SHEETS ON PAGES 28 TO 30

What can we do?

This sheet links temperature to activity.

The children should colour the outer band red if the activity requires hot weather (summer) or blue if it requires cold weather (winter). Seasonal activities should be discussed as a class or in groups.

How hot is it?

This sheet is designed to help children appreciate the range of temperatures around them. It is also of value in their estimation and recording work.

Ask the children, either singly or in groups, to estimate the temperature of each object on the sheet and to draw lines linking the objects to the appropriate points on the thermometer.

Most of their judgements will be based on direct experience and it is valuable to encourage consideration of 'hotter/colder than' in terms of estimating relative values.

'Actual' temperatures can be checked by using thermometers.

Activities involving hot objects must be carefully supervised. Boiling water should not be measured by the children.

The radiators should be 'on'. The hot water should be from the tap the children normally use. Body temperature should be taken in the way illustrated - not in the mouth.

The school-kitchen staff can be approached to provide a hot meal prior to lunchtime so that its temperature can be checked in the classroom.

Air temperatures

Here the children should estimate the temperatures at which certain activities take place. In Britain, in recent years, the temperature has rarely slipped below 0°C in daytime for a prolonged period. So, outdoor skating is outside the experience of most infant-age children.

A 'good' sunbathing day would be between 23 and 30°C.

The highest recorded temperature is 58°C (Libya) and the lowest (excluding Antarctica, which is not inhabited) is −68°C (Soviet Union).

Comparisons of the two sheets should help the children to identify the great difference between what we regard as a 'hot' day (30°C) and 'hot' water (boiling point 100°C).

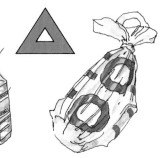

Completely fill a plastic (not glass) water bottle with water.

Place in a plastic carrier bag (no holes) and put in a freezer overnight.

When water freezes, it expands. The force of expansion can break a glass container or split a metal pipe.

When would you first discover a burst?

How can we stop a water pipe from bursting?

Measuring instruments

A thermometer measures how hot or cold something is. Three widely used types are: liquid (alcohol or mercury) in glass, Thermostiks and electronic/digital.

Each type can record and 'save' the lowest and highest temperature recorded since last reset.

WHAT CAN WE DO?

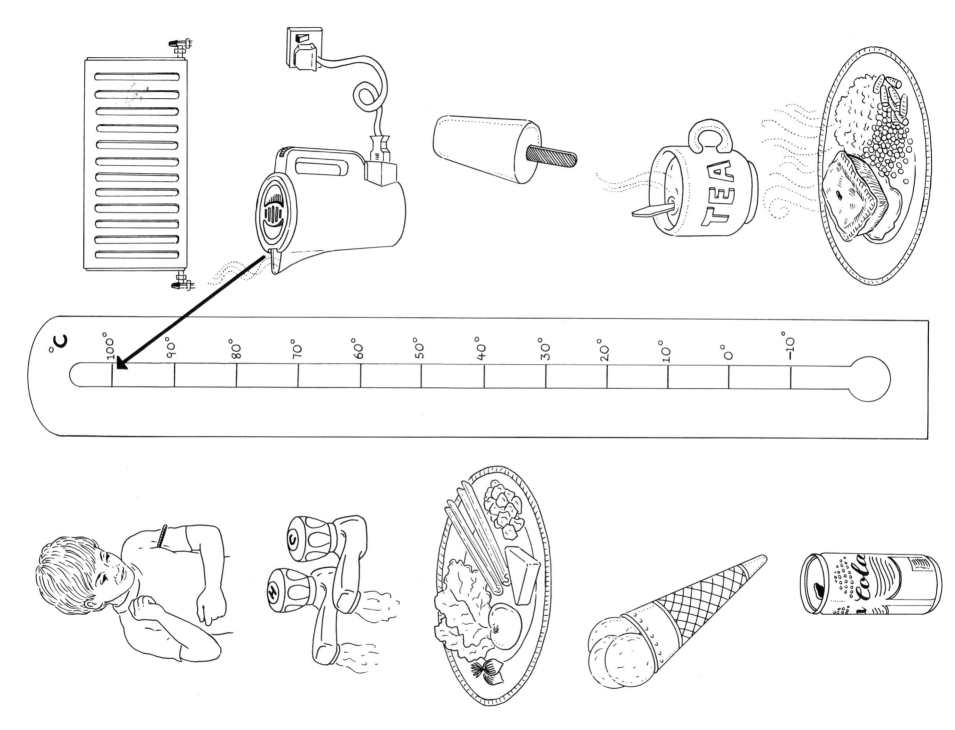

°C

100°
90°
80°
70°
60°
50°
40°
30°
20°
10°
0°
−10°

TEA

Cola

AIR TEMPERATURES

Today

°C
100°
90°
80°
70°
60°
50°
40°
30°
20°
10°
0°
−10°

UPS AND DOWNS

100°	99°	98°	97°	96°	95°	94°	93°	92°	91°
81°	82°	83°	84°	85°	86°	87°	88°	89°	90°
80°	79°	78°	77°	76°	75°	74°	73°	72°	71°
61°	62°	63°	64°	65°	66°	67°	68°	69°	70°
60°	59°	58°	57°	56°	55°	54°	53°	52°	51°
41°	42°	43°	44°	45°	46°	47°	48°	49°	50°
40°	39°	38°	37°	36°	35°	34°	33°	32°	31°
21°	22°	23°	24°	25°	26°	27°	28°	29°	30°
20°	19°	18°	17°	16°	15°	14°	13°	12°	11°
1°	2°	3°	4°	5°	6°	7°	8°	9°	10°

UPS AND DOWNS

Playing the game

The board consists of 100 squares, numbered 1 to 100. Each square represents a point on the Celsius scale. Each number is annotated with the degree symbol.

The game proceeds like Snakes and Ladders. Each picture on the board which depicts a source of heat – the volcano, the boiler, the cup of tea, the sun and the log fire – is the foot of a 'ladder', which is itself an extension of the source: for example, the volcano and its plume-of-smoke 'ladder'. When a player lands on the base of one of these pictures, he or she immediately ascends to the top of the 'ladder': for example, 4° to 64°.

Each feature which depicts coldness – the skier, the icicle, the ice-cream, the snowfall, and the icy slide – is the head of a 'snake'. When a player lands at the top of one of the pictures, he or she descends immediately to the tail-end of the 'snake': for example, 95° to 35°.

Up to six children can play on a single enlarged board (see below).

It is valuable to allow the children to discuss how they think the game should be played and how the pictures ought to be divided into two categories.

Making the board

Photocopy the game board on page 31, mount the copy on card, then colour and laminate it. You will need to prepare several boards – likewise the spinner and counters.

If you have access to an enlarging photocopier, blow up the size of the board to the maximum enlargement available. The counters will also need enlarging but the spinner should stay the same size.

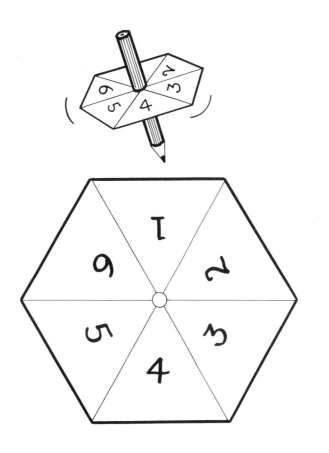

The degree Celsius (°C) is the standard unit for measuring temperature. The parents and older relatives of many children will still be using the degree Fahrenheit (°F) where they have a choice.

Invite the children to produce a hot and cold game for older members of their families. How many squares will it need? What are the start and finish points? They should design and make the board, choosing different images to those used on the Celsius board. They should also design and make the accompanying spinner and counters.

The children should consider 'themes' which would be appropriate for the board game yet linked to temperature, such as 'Energy Efficiency', 'Global Warming', 'Holiday Activities', 'Seasons'.

There is no reason why, once designed, the product should not become the focus of a mini-enterprise, be produced, packaged, marketed and sold. The proceeds could go towards buying weather equipment or as a contribution to a charity offering relief to the victims of natural disasters.

The following two algorithms convert one temperature scale to the other.

To convert °F to °C

Example 212°F to °C
1 Subtract	32	212 − 32 = 180
2 Multiply by	5	180 × 5 = 900
3 Divide by	9	900 ÷ 9 = 100°C

To convert °C to °F

Example 20°C to °F
1 Multiply by	9	20 × 9 = 180
2 Divide by	5	180 ÷ 5 = 36
3 Add	32	36 + 32 = 68°F

Each of the previous sections has included ways of recording an aspect of the weather. The constituent parts of the weather can now be brought together to form daily or weekly weather records, which can be presented in a variety of ways. Pages 34 to 37, 39 and 40 may be photocopied for individuals or groups so that they can maintain their own records.

When should observations be made? Consistency and fairness in making observations should be discussed, particularly the need for regular times and locations of observation. This is illustrated by the hourly temperature chart (page 21) and the question 'What is today's temperature?'

Weather greatly affects people's lives. Often our first thoughts in the morning concern the clothes we shall wear. Any discussion about this should be handled sensitively, as some children may be dressed inappropriately. Page 34 provides an opportunity to match footwear to weather conditions, the children linking illustrations by drawing connecting lines. The theme can be developed by collecting, analysing and displaying information about clothes: for example, those worn by pupils, or seen on a TV programme or from pages 13 and 14.

Type of day / Type of clothes	WET	WINDY	SUNNY	COLD
(boots, umbrella)	✓			
(t-shirt)			✓	
(jumper)				✓

The information can be transferred to a computer database, stored, displayed and analysed.

Symbols

The children should consider the variety and types of symbols. Page 35 offers ready-made symbols, but the children may create their own designs. How many symbols are needed? Too few is limiting, too many can lead to confusion and lessen their effectiveness. Use TV weather reports and newspaper forecast maps. The children can evaluate, create or modify as appropriate. Their symbols can be used on a wall map or on a photocopy of page 69.

'Today is …', on page 37, includes a clock face so that consistency in the timing of recording is reinforced. Keep and store weather records. They will be useful for making comparisons in a different season and for other groups to call upon. Compare temperatures in winter and summer, or from one year to the next.

Does the past predict the future? Weather forecasters look for particular patterns in weather behaviour. They have thousands of weather stations around the globe feeding information to the world's biggest computers, yet weather forecasting is so complex, that a success rate of 80% is considered high. We cannot hope to challenge this figure, but this should not prevent children from attempting to forecast tomorrow's weather, based upon their recordings. Can we predict the afternoon's weather? Compare the local weather forecast with the national forecast, or a newspaper forecast with a TV forecast. Which wins?

Mock up your own weather 'broadcast'. A large cardboard box makes an excellent 'sit-in TV'. Budding meteorologists can hone their skills in front of the rest of the class. Make a video recording of your weather forecast – the local secondary school may wish to help here.

Temp °C chart (M M Tu Tu W W Th Th F F) with Key: Summer, Winter

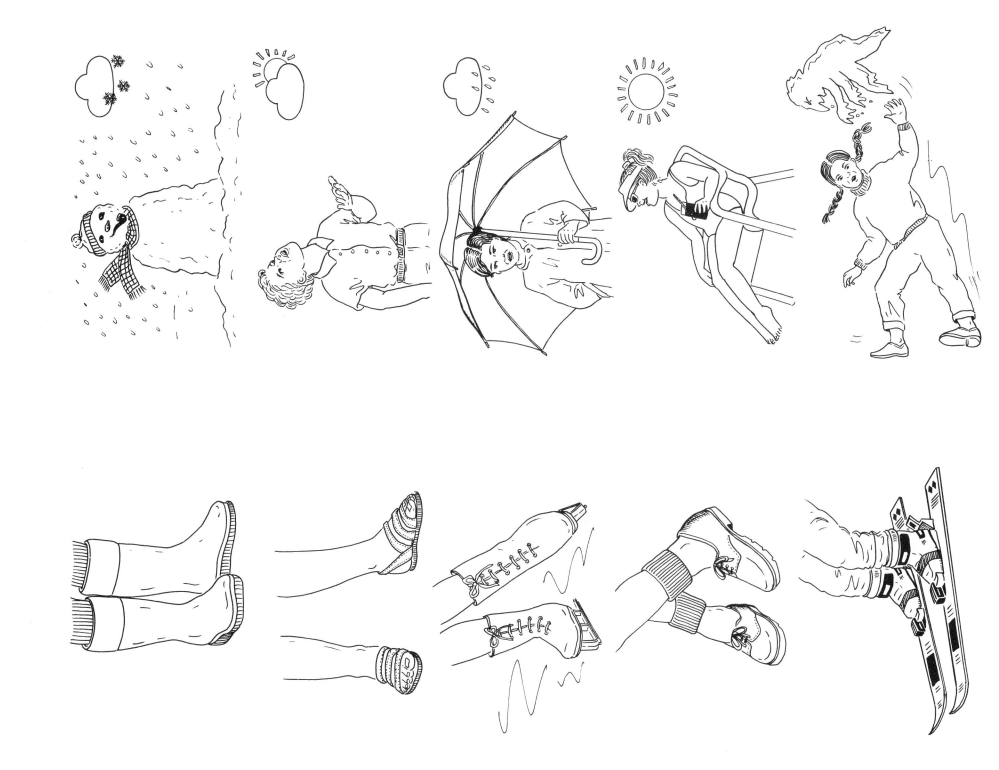

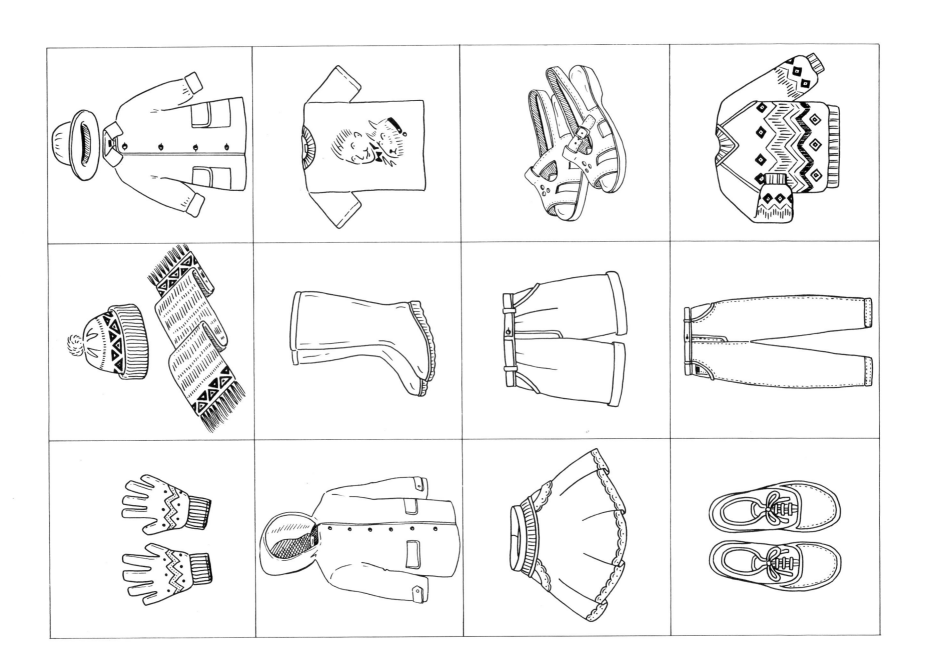

TODAY IS ...

Today is _____

The weather today

Clothes for today

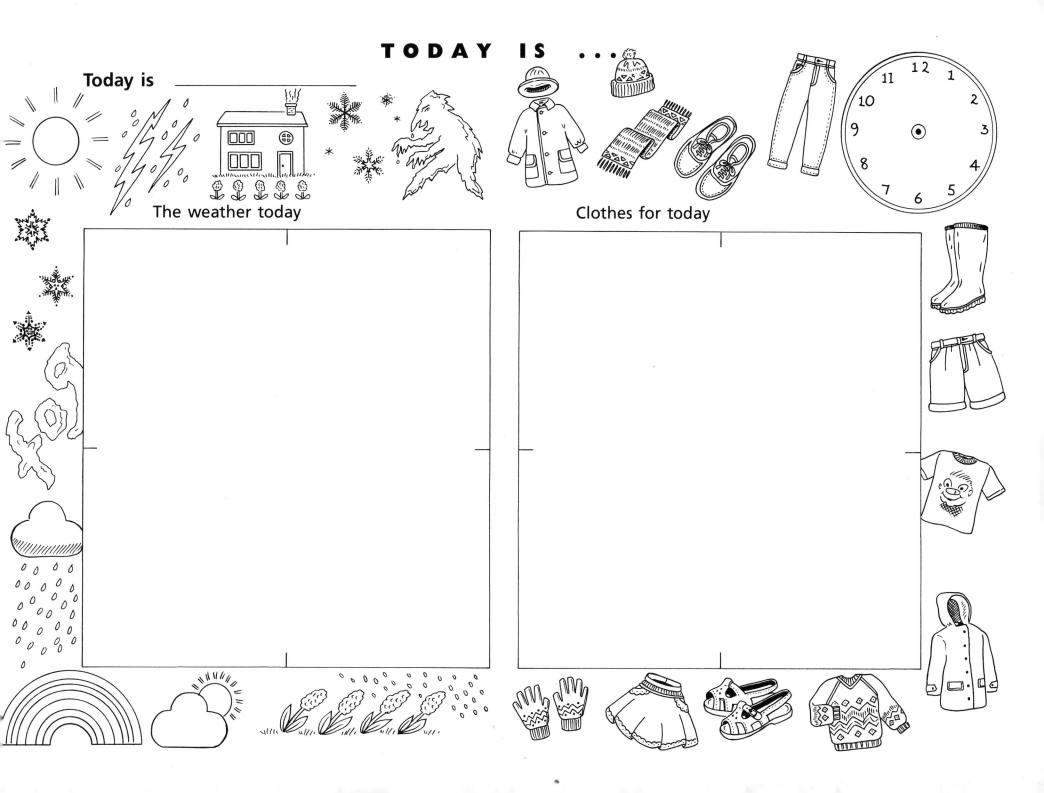

A vital part of meteorology is the visual observation of the atmosphere around us. Looking at the sky can tell us about the forthcoming weather, especially in the short term. For example, the afternoon's weather can be forecast by observing the clouds, their type and direction of movement.

Sunshine

Direct observation of the sun is dangerous. On no account should the children look at the sun. Instead, observe the effect of shadows. By studying the length and movement of the shadow of a metre rule, the apparent motion of the sun across the sky can be recorded. The weekly record should be stored so that seasonal comparisons may be made (the lower winter sun will produce longer shadows). Always work to Standard Time. This activity provides an opportunity to consider seasonal day lengths and time zones around the world, and the chance to make a sundial.

Sunlight is an energy source. Space stations and satellites use solar cells to convert sunlight into electricity. Some watches and calculators are also powered by solar cells. The children can investigate solar power by connecting a 12 V solar cell to a small electric motor. The more sunlight that falls on the solar cell, the more electricity is made and the faster the motor turns. Stick a piece of paper to the motor spindle and count the revolutions per minute. Always ensure that the cell is placed in the same position to make the tests fair.

Weather records often show 'hours of sunshine'. This is measured using a Campbell-Stokes sunshine recorder, in which a ball of glass acts like a lens to burn a piece of paper. As the sun 'moves' across the sky, a trace is burnt into the paper. The length of the scorch marks records the hours of sunshine.

Clouds are masses of water droplets or ice particles (depending upon the height of the cloud). Clouds can occur at heights just above ground level to 14 000 metres. They are classified according to height (high 6–14 km, medium 2–6 km and low surface–2 km) and type. There are three main types of cloud: cumulus (heaps), cirrus (curls) and stratus (layers). Combinations of the basic cloud types constitute further types. For example, cirrostratus is a high-altitude layered cloud of ice crystals. Rain bearing clouds are called nimbus.

Type	Height	Description	Associated Weather
Cirrus	High	Separate white whispy bands, often with 'curl'.	May bring storms after a period of good weather.
Stratus	Low	Blanket of low, grey cloud which can reach to ground level.	Drizzle and fog.
Cumulus	Low	Fluffy, white flat-bottomed clouds which look like cotton wool.	Small cumulus – fair Large cumulus – showers
Nimbostratus	Medium	Large dark cloud reaching from ground to several thousand metres.	Heavy rain.
Cumulonimbus	Low to high	Can be dark at base, towering high to white smooth anvil-shaped head.	Very heavy showers, hail, thunder and lightning.

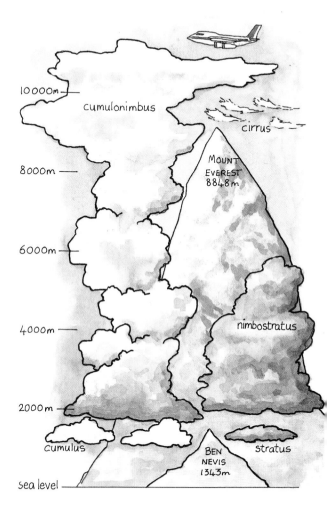

Type of cloud and/or the amount of cloud cover can be recorded. Meteorologists measure cloud cover in oktas or eighths of the sky. This is quite difficult to do: look straight up and estimate. A simpler method would be to look out of the same window each day in order to estimate cloud cover.

Name: _____ Date: _____

Draw a picture of the sky and name the type of cloud

Cloud type	Cloud type	Cloud type	Cloud type	Cloud type

Day

1 _____ 2 _____ 3 _____ 4 _____ 5 _____

1 Cirrus: whispy clouds

2 Stratus: high clouds— like a sheet

3 Cumulus: small fluffy clouds that drift across the sky

4 Nimbostratus: rain and storm clouds

WEEKLY WEATHER RECORD

Date _____

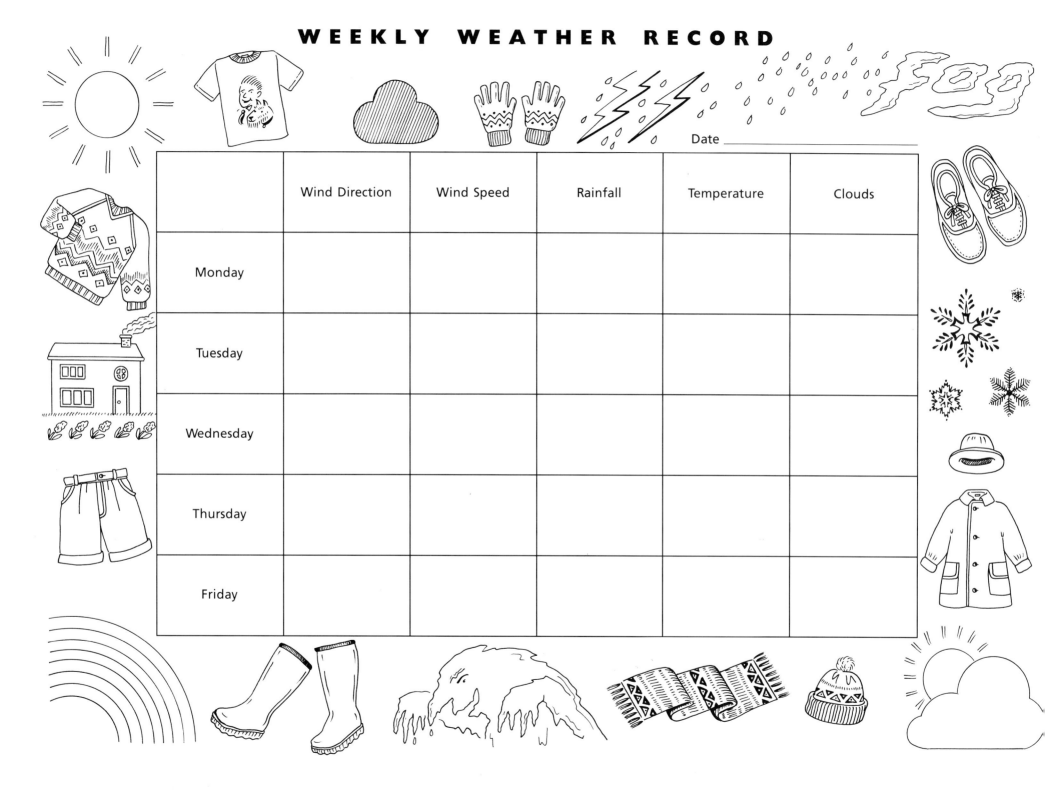

	Wind Direction	Wind Speed	Rainfall	Temperature	Clouds
Monday					
Tuesday					
Wednesday					
Thursday					
Friday					

Weather forecasting is an increasingly exact science, relying on vast amounts of data from a variety of sources. Despite popular opinion to the contrary, weather forecasters are improving the accuracy of their forecasts. Satellite information and the capacity of computers to handle billions of calculations per second has revolutionised weather forecasting. Even so there is still a place for the amateur. We can all make forecasts based on our own observations, experiences and intuition – and children should be encouraged to make oral forecasts.

Folklore

Having checked the accuracy of their own forecasts, the children should move on to assess traditional weather sayings in the same way. Some sayings are national but others are regional or local and the class can collect these. Traditional nursery rhymes are a handy starting point.

The north wind doth blow
And we shall have snow,
And what will poor robin do then?
Poor thing!

He'll sit in a barn,
To keep himself warm,
And hide his head under his wing.
Poor thing!

Here we come gathering nuts in May,
Nuts in May, nuts in May,
Here we come gathering nuts in May
On a cold and frosty morning.

*Is May a frosty month?
Often? rarely?*

*Try to link rhymes and sayings.
Do they give the same message?*

Cast ne'er a clout
Till May be out.

There are two interpretations of this old saying. Both refer to wearing warm clothes (clout) but in one 'May' means the month of May, in the other it means the May blossom (hawthorn).

Is there a connection between the north wind and snow? Is there a general connection between wind direction and temperature? The children can suggest ways of checking. They can also observe whether the robin stays in Britain in winter.

Some sayings are easily checked.

Red Sky at night
Shepherd's delight,
Red Sky at morning
Shepherd's warning.

(Also popular as 'sailor's delight'.)

Rain before seven
Fine before eleven.

A sunshiny shower
won't last half an hour.

St Swithin
If rain falls on St Swithin's Day, 15 July, it will rain for the following 40 days.

This particular saying originated in AD 971, when plans to move the bones of St Swithin from outside to inside Winchester Cathedral had to be postponed because of continuous rain. It was seen as divine intervention!

What is perhaps even more miraculous is that the saying is still in use despite being disproved almost annually since.

NATURE WATCH

The children should also check the folklore which suggests, for example, that

Birds build nests earlier/later before a bad/good summer.

Cows lie down when rain is on the way.

Spiders spin smaller webs when gales are due.

Bushes (especially holly) produce extra berries before a bad winter.

Having analysed the sayings against their own observations and records, the children should discuss 'logical' connections. For example, perhaps nest-building is linked to the spring weather (as in the remarkable spring of 1990 when so many birds built early), or perhaps berries are likely to be more numerous after a good summer/autumn than before a hard winter.

Local links

Try to invite a local amateur forecaster into school to talk to the children. If you don't know of anyone, contact the local library or local radio station to recommend a suitable person. You should brief the forecaster fully before the visit. Explain just what you are hoping for and describe the age and interests of the children.

The use of vivid images and highly imaginative comparisons are common in weather writing. The children will be motivated to be adventurous in their own writing if they have heard and read how others have responded to the weather.

There is the traditional verse:
Mackerel sky, mackerel sky,
Not long wet and not long dry.
Mackerel sky, mackerel sky,
Not long wet and not long dry.

or Gerald Manley Hopkins' description of the night sky in cloudless conditions:
Look at the stars! Look, look up at the skies!
O look at all the fire-folk sitting in the air!

or Wordsworth's response to the rainbow:
My heart leaps up when I behold
A rainbow in the sky.

Children should have opportunities to read, hear or repeat certain well-known phrases and sayings and consider their meanings — both surface and deeper meanings.

Mad dogs and Englishmen go out in the mid-day sun.
N. Coward

Somewhere the sun is shining.
C.K. Harris

The night has a thousand eyes,
And the day but one;
Yet the light of the bright world dies,
With the dying sun.
Bourdillon

Some recent poetry has addressed the issue of environmental awareness. The following poem combines current concerns about the weather with a traditional nursery rhyme.

Twinkle twinkle little star,
How I wonder what you are.
Up above the world so high,
Like a diamond in the sky.

If the sky stays pure and clean,
We will see your twinkle bright.
But smoke, exhaust, and acid rain
All will cloud your flickering light.

Twinkle twinkle little star,
I'd like to keep you as you are.

WEATHER WORDS

The theme of weather offers an opportunity for children to extend their vocabulary and use some words which are specific to the study of weather.

Weather words may be associated by **senses:**

SIGHTS: clouds, rainbows, sunbeams, dawn, dusk, fog, mist, dew.

SOUNDS: thunder, wind, rain, leaves rustling, ice cracking, snow crunching, splashing.

FEEL: frozen, warm, wet, dry, damp, chilly, sunburnt.

Or by season:

WINTER: dark, cold, snow, frost, blizzard, thermal clothing, skiing, scarves.

SUMMER: hot, light, drought, water, ice-cream, arid, blisters, forest fire.

Or by type:

WIND: gust, gale, breeze, hurricane, chill-factor, bitter, zephyr.

WEATHER IN MYTHOLOGY

Most cultures have stories relating to the weather, and many have myths and legends which identify gods and other supernatural beings with aspects of the weather.

In the mythology of Ancient Greece, Zeus's symbol was the thunderbolt, and Poseidon was responsible for earthquakes and sea storms. In northern European legend, Thor too has the symbol of the thunderbolt. When thunder was heard, it was Thor's chariot, pulled by giant goats, roaring across the heavens. Lightning occurred when Thor threw his blazing weapon to earth. The Sun symbol was associated with Odin (Wodan). In Rome, Jupiter was god of light and of lightning. In Hindu mythology, Agni was the sun in heaven, lightning in the air and fire on earth.

The Christian halo is probably the remnants of the symbol for the sun, whose worship was replaced by the new religion.

Some of the History Study Units in the National Curriculum are concerned with societies which had ceremonies, beliefs and practices linked to the weather. Opportunities exist for links to be made between history and weather: Invaders and Settlers (Romans, Anglo-Saxons and Vikings), Exploration and Encounters 1450-1550 (Aztec civilisation), Ancient Egypt, Ancient Greece, Mesopotamia, Assyria, The Indus Valley, The Maya.

WEATHER POEMS

Hearing, reading, responding to and writing poetry have always been an important part of primary education whatever the topic. Weather features richly in the poetry.

The selection on this page and on pages 44 and 45 ranges from the simple rhyme, through the traditional, to the recent and amusing. It is intended that there should be something for all ages and tastes but it still represents only a small sample of the wealth of material available.

RAIN
Rain, rain
go away
Come again
another day.

Rain
Rain on the
green grass
Rain on the tree
Rain on the
housetop
But not on me.

CLOUDS
White sheep, white sheep
On a blue hill
When the wind stops
You all stand still.

You all run away
When the winds blow.
White sheep, white sheep
Where do you go?

The Fight of the Year

And there goes the bell for the third month
and Winter comes out of its corner looking groggy
Spring leads with a left to the head
followed by a sharp right to the body
    daffodils
    primroses
    crocuses
    snowdrops
    lilacs
    violets
    pussywillow
Winter can't take much more punishment
and Spring shows no sign of tiring
    tadpoles
    squirrels
    baalambs
    badgers
    bunny rabbits
    mad march hares
    horses and hounds
Spring is merciless
Winter won't go the full twelve rounds
    bobtail clouds
    scallywaggy winds
    the sun
    a pavement artist
    in every town
A left to the chin
and Winter's down!
    tomatoes
    radish
    onions
    beetroot
    celery
    and any
    amount
    of lettuce
    for dinner
Winter's out for the count
Spring is the winner!

Roger McGough

The Months

January cold desolate;
February all dripping wet;
March wind ranges;
April changes;
Birds sing in tune
To flowers of May,
And sunny June
Brings longest day;
In scorched July
The storm-clouds fly
Lightning-torn
August bears corn.
September fruit;
In rough October
Earth must disrobe her;
Stars fall and shoot
In keen November;
And night is long
And cold is strong
In bleak December.

Christina Rossetti

Rain

I opened my eyes
And looked up at the rain
And it dripped in my head
And flowed into my brain
So pardon this wild crazy thing I just said
I'm just not the same since there's rain in my head.
I step very softly
I walk very slow
I can't do a hand-stand
Or I might overflow.
And all I can hear as I lie in my bed
Is the slishity-slosh of the rain in my head.

Shel Silverstein

It's Winter, It's Winter

It's winter, it's winter, it's wonderful winter,
When everyone lounges around in the sun!

It's winter, it's winter, it's wonderful winter,
When everyone's brown like a steak overdone!

It's winter, it's winter, it's wonderful winter,
It's swimming and surfing and hunting for conkers!

It's winter, it's winter, it's wonderful winter,
And I am completely and utterly bonkers!

Kit Wright

Death of a Snowman

I was awake all night,
Big as a polar bear,
Strong and firm and white.
The tall black hat I wear
Was draped with ermine fur.
I felt so fit and well
Till the world began to stir.
And the morning sun swell.
I was tired, began to yawn;
At noon in the humming sun
I caught a severe warm;
My nose began to run.
My hat grew black and fell,
Was followed by my grey head.
There was no funeral bell,
But by tea-time I was dead.

Vernon Scannell

Bed in Summer

In winter I get up at night
And dress by yellow candle-light.
In summer, quite the other way,
I have to go to bed by day.

I have to go to bed and see
The birds still hopping on the tree,
Or hear the grown-up people's feet
Still going past me in the street.

And does it not seem hard to you,
When all the sky is clear and blue
And I should like so much to play,
To have to go to bed by day?

R.L. Stevenson

Winter Morning

Winter is the king of showmen,
Turning tree stumps into snow men
And houses into birthday cakes
And spreading sugar over the lakes.
Smooth and clean and frost white
The world looks good enough to bite.
That's the season to be young,
Catching snowflakes on your tongue.

Snow is snowy when it's snowing
I'm sorry it's slushy when it's going.

Ogden Nash

Sir Winter

I heard Sir Winter coming.
He crept out of his bed
and rubbed his thin and freezing hands:
'I'll soon be up!' he said.

'I'll shudder at the keyhole
and rattle at the door,
I'll strip the trees of all their leaves
and strew them on the floor;

'I'll harden every puddle
that Autumn thinks is his –
I'll lay a sparkling quilt of snow
on everything that is!

'I'll bring a load of darkness
as large as any coal,
and drive my husky dogs across
the world, from pole to pole.

'Oho! How you will shiver!'
And then I heard him say:
'But in the middle of it all
I'll give you CHRISTMAS DAY!'

Jean Kenward

Use a database program on your computer to store, recall, compare and display your weather records.

Use a database which is appropriate for the children's abilities and experience: for example, OURFACTS. This has a weather file from which you select the depth and range of data.

BEWARE
Some programs will allow 'silly' entries to be made.

Careful preparation will allow consistency of output when records are recalled and compared.

Initially collect only four types of information. Use only N S E W, measure in mm and °C, and describe wind strength as still, breezy, windy.

	Mon	Tues
Wind direction	W	
Wind strength	windy	
Rain (in mm)	2mm	
Temperature	12°c	

Record the findings each day at the same time and enter them on to a database. At least two weeks data is needed before any meaningful displays can be produced.

DATA INTERPRETATION QUESTIONS

Simple interpretation

How many days did it rain?
What was the temperature on Friday?
How much rainfall altogether?
From which direction does the wind blow most often?

Seeing patterns

Does the north wind bring rain?
When the temperature is low, from which direction does the wind blow?
Does it rain on warm days?

Consider other sources of weather information.

Use newspapers, radio, TV, to gather weather information.

How accurate is the information?

Keep a record.

Day	TV forecast	Actual Weather	Accuracy
Mon	Rain	Sunny	0/10
Tues	Rain	Showers	6/10

Which forecasts are most accurate?

MONDAY	Forecast	Actual
Local		
Regional		
National		
TUESDAY		

You may have a Teletext television in school. Ceefax pages 580-590 and Oracle pages 300 onwards offer a wealth of weather data: local, regional, national and international forecasts and records.

DATA INTERPRETATION QUESTIONS

In which cities was the temperature over 20°C yesterday?
Which city had the highest rainfall?

No Teletext?

Teletext decoders are available which plug into your computer. They cost about £100.

Attach the decoder to your TV aerial lead and the computer will give you all the Teletext information. These can be printed out so that comparisons can be made across days, weeks, months.

There is a number of telephone information lines giving weather forecasts for your area, plus other areas of the UK, or holiday destinations abroad. National newspapers list the appropriate numbers.

Note: these services are usually prefixed 0898 and can be expensive. Children should be warned not to use the telephone at home without parental permission.

Weather service

Produce your own weather service. Your word-processing program or desk-top publishing software will enable the children to publish, televise and broadcast their forecast around school.

Design a weather newsheet for the school.

Make a video of your weather forecasters. Also a radio broadcast could be made using a tape recorder.

CONCEPT KEYBOARD OVERLAY

When I go outside, I feel		very cold		cold		cool		warm		hot		very hot

Temperature °C	−5	−4	−3	−2	−1	0	1	2	3	4	5	6	7	8
	9	10	11	12	13	14	15	16	17	18	19	20	21	22
	23	24	25	26	27	28	29	30	Control the cursor					

The wind is coming from the	North	South	East	West	RETURN	←	→
Monday	Tuesday	Wednesday	Thursday	Friday	DELETE	↑	↓

The Concept Keyboard is a pressure-sensitive board which enables children to input information into a computer with a single touch. The photocopiable overlay opposite may be used to input weather information into your computer. Colour and laminate your overlay to make a bright, long-lasting resource. This overlay links

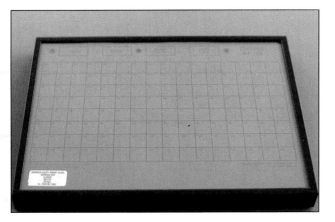

'feeling' with temperature, the sky and wind direction. Design your own overlay to reflect your experiment linking rainfall with wind direction, or wind direction with temperature. A program such as PROMPT or WRITER is used to prepare words, prompts or headings on the screen, the answers to which are supplied with a single press of an appropriate area of the overlay.

The program also organises which areas of the keyboard relate to the symbol on the overlay. Initial preparation takes some time but, once done, can be used indefinitely by children of all abilities and by those whose motor control precludes their use of a normal keyboard.

Children at Key Stage 1 could match pictures taken from a story book with sentences on the computer screen. Using, for example, 'The Rainbow Balloon' by Fredun Shapur (Simon and

Schuster) we could ask the children to carry out a cloze procedure using weather words, and discuss the powerful effect that weather has on our lives.

The pictures on pages 13 and 14 may be converted into overlays and 'find the object' questions given on screen. When the child presses the correct area of the overlay, the matching word appears on screen, enhancing language understanding. It may also be used for assessment purposes.

Sequencing is a skill which may be taught or assessed linking a story with an overlay, with weather conditions providing a central theme.

The board game from page 31 may be modified with 'forfeit' or 'reward' displayed on screen. When the counter lands on a 'choice' square, a press on the appropriate Concept Keyboard area will reveal the consequence — either advance or

retreat so many squares — along with the weather reason.

Other pages from this book may be converted into overlays. For example, the satellite photographs may be used for identifying weather fronts, or areas of the UK suitable for certain specific types of farming.

Classification of experience (for example, strength or speed of the wind) could be related to wind effects in the playground and recorded on the Keyboard. Make your own wind classification. Compare your results with the Beaufort Scale on page 64.

A variety of databases is available for children at Key Stages 1 and 2. Upper juniors should display and compare two variables, such as temperature and rainfall, over a period of time. Some programs contain databanks which can be drawn on (see also page 66).

Campus 2000

Campus 2000 is a national data and information service which can be accessed from the classroom.

On payment of a subscription (see page 79), you can connect to the Campus 2000 service via a modem (a device which allows computer signals to travel along a telephone line). Using the school computer, children can search for weather data and exchange weather information with schools around the world for the cost of a local telephone call.

Fax

Many schools have installed facsimile transmission (fax) machines as office aids, and more will. They provide immediate and cost-effective transfer of black-and-white copy, including photographs and diagrams. They are therefore useful for sending weather maps between schools.

Use the outline map of the British Isles on page 69 as a base sheet (Gall projection). The children should record the weather in their school's locality, using symbols for temperature, rainfall, wind speed and direction, and cloud cover. This weather record can then be faxed to a school in another region, where their local data is added. The expanded record is then faxed to yet another school – and so on. By linking several UK schools, a national weather picture can be established in minutes. The last school in the chain faxes the 'whole picture' to the others. Take turns in the sequence of recording in order to even out the costs.

Campus 2000, fax machines and satellite data require capital expenditure. Some schools unable to afford them have borrowed equipment from local colleges, schools and businesses. Others have received sponsorship for equipment and/or subscription costs from local companies. As fax technology improves, some companies write off obsolescent equipment. So, let your business contacts know you would be interested.

Satellites

Signals from weather satellites can easily be received in school. The children can use prediction software to find out when a weather satellite will pass overhead. A simple aerial can be used to pick up the satellite's signals. The signals are fed into the school's computer to produce a weather picture.

Pages 70 and 71 are satellite photographs of the British Isles. Page 70 shows a completely clear day – no cloud cover; page 71 a weather system moving in from the west. Note the distinctive swirl of a low-pressure system bringing cloud and rain from the west.

The children can compare the two photographs. They can describe the weather conditions that people on the ground would experience. Discussion should include consideration of the time of year, the weather effects later that day and over night, and a comparison of the conditions depicted with present conditions to see whether they 'match'.

Humidity is the amount of moisture (water vapour) in the air. The warmer the air, the more water vapour it can hold.

Relative humidity is the amount of water vapour in the air, expressed as a percentage of the maximum amount of water vapour that could be held by the air at that temperature.

.... and the temperature in Singapore is 30°C with 90% humidity

At 100% humidity, the air is saturated with water vapour and this vapour may then be seen as mist, fog or a cloud. This phenomenon may be seen in the bathroom when a hot bath is run.

We may feel the humidity on a 'muggy' warm day. We can also see the effects of different humidity levels in the world around us.

The water vapour escaping from the top of a power station drifts up into the atmosphere. On a dry day, the vapour is quickly absorbed into the air. On a slightly humid day, the vapour travels a little way before it disappears.

Washing will dry quicker on a less humid day.

Water vapour in the air can produce dew, ground frost, or early morning fog after a clear night.

How can we measure humidity?

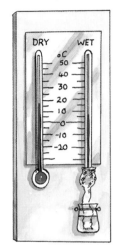

A wet-and-dry thermometer works on the phenomenon of cooling by evaporation. Two identical thermometers are set side by side. The bulb of one is surrounded by a wick which passes down into a reservoir of pure water. As water is drawn up the wick, it evaporates. The drier the air the more water evaporates. The evaporating water takes energy (heat) from the bulb and the wet-temperature reading falls. The difference between the two readings is a measure of the humidity.

If the humidity is 100%, no evaporation takes place and so the temperatures will be the same.

DRY   WET

Try this outside

The wet glove feels colder as the water evaporates.

A combined thermometer/ hygrometer measures temperature and humidity percentages. It is cheap – less than £2.

Cobalt chloride paper is blue when dry, pinky white when damp or wet. Re-use after drying in an oven. Twenty sheets of strips cost about £1.50.

Using natural materials

A human hair is shorter when dry. It absorbs moisture from the air when the humidity is high, which increases its length. We can use this behaviour to make a hair humidity meter (see page 53).

Pluck a hair from a willing volunteer. Tape it to the top of the card and to the lever, close to its pivot. Any small change in the length of the hair will be magnified by the length of the arrow. Compare your hygrometer readings with the position of the arrow. Movement of the arrow is slow, and it may not move discernibly for many days if the humidity remains constant.

Create a damp atmosphere in the kitchen. Take in the hair meter and observe.

Seaweed feels damp before rain appears because it absorbs moisture from the air.

Animal gut – often known as catgut – is made of many strands of animal gut twisted together. On a dry day, it untwists. On a damp day, the twist tightens. This effect is used in a weather house.

Catgut is not made from the gut of a cat but usually (in Europe) from the gut of a sheep. The word catgut has evolved from the animal gut used to string a 'kit' – a small violin used by dancing masters in the 18th century. Cat or animal gut can be obtained from tennis racket stringers. Ask for the non-weatherproof type so that the moisture can penetrate the fibres.

The man and woman are fastened to a support, hung on a length of catgut. The moisture in the air affects the amount of twist in the gut and the man (damp or wet conditions) or woman (dry) swing out from the front of the house.

Gardeners often want to increase the humidity around their plants and prevent the loss of moisture. They do this by covering the top of the plant with a plastic bag.

Large amounts of water vapour are returned to the atmosphere from leaves. That is why rainforests are hot and humid.

Place two similar plants side by side. Envelop one with a clear plastic bag. Leave overnight. Cut a slit in the top of the bag and drop a piece of dry, blue cobalt chloride paper on to each set of leaves.

The air around the enveloped plant will be more humid. The paper will turn white quickly, showing a more humid atmosphere. Drops of moisture should also be visible on the bag.

Dehumidifiers

These are now commonly used in winter to reduce moisture in the home.

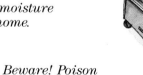 Beware! Poison

Silica gel is packed with cameras and electrical equipment. It absorbs moisture, thus preventing damage from the effects of dampness.

HOW HUMID?

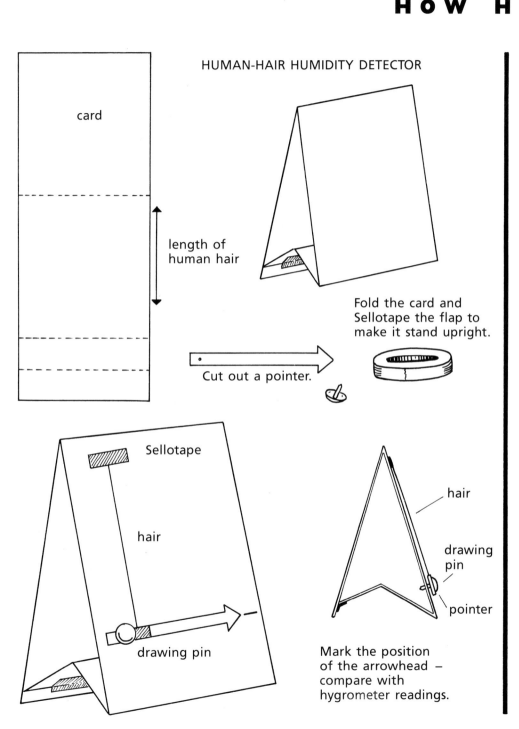

HUMAN-HAIR HUMIDITY DETECTOR

card

length of human hair

Fold the card and Sellotape the flap to make it stand upright.

Cut out a pointer.

Sellotape

hair

hair

drawing pin

hair

drawing pin

pointer

Mark the position of the arrowhead – compare with hygrometer readings.

WEATHER HOUSE

DRY WET

Cut a slot or make a hole in cork or wood. Glue gut into the hole or slot. The top should be gripped by the roof.

This could be a flat roof.

Notice the twist of the gut.

Make figures out of card or Lego.

Make walls out of Lego, Brio, Sticklebricks or Mobilo.

RISING DAMP

EXPERIMENT 1

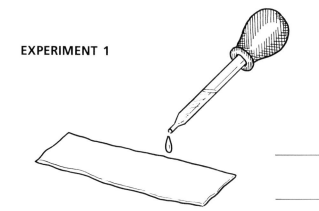

What happens when water is dropped on to dry blue cobalt chloride paper?

_____

_____

_____

Put the damp cobalt chloride paper over a radiator. Leave it for a while. What happens?

_____

_____

Cobalt chloride paper is **blue** when dry. Your teacher may need to dry the paper before starting if it is not blue. This may be done in a warm oven for a few minutes.

EXPERIMENT 2

Three identical 3 litre plastic Cola bottles are marked 1,2 and 3.

 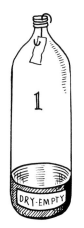  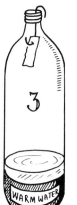

Put the paper in each bottle at the same time.

Which paper changes colour first? _____

Which paper changes colour last? _____

How long does it take?

First _____

Last _____

EXPERIMENT 3

Place a saucer of table salt on a window sill. Leave it overnight.

How does the salt feel when you first put it out?

_____

How does the salt feel the following day?

_____

Why do you think it has changed?

_____

Lightning

The friction between water droplets, or ice particles, moving in a cumulonimbus cloud, produces positive (+) and negative (−) electrical charges. Typically, the positive charges accumulate in the upper part of the cloud, the negative in the lower part. As the total electrical charge builds up, a point is reached when the electrical insulation of the air in the cloud breaks down and electrical arcing − a lightning strike − occurs. This is called 'sheet' lightning. Sometimes, the charge on the lower part of the cloud discharges to a high point on the ground, such as a tree, where an 'induced' opposite charge has built up. This is called 'fork' lightning.

The induced charge collecting on a pointed lightning conductor on a tall building is conducted to earth by a thick copper cable connected to a large metal plate buried in the earth. There is no build-up of charge, thus no lightning can discharge to the building.

Thunder

Thunder is the 'noise' made by lightning. Because sound travels much slower than light, thunder is heard some 3 seconds after the lightning is seen. Sound travels at 330 m/s, light at 300 000 000 m/s. So, sound takes 3 seconds to travel 1 km, light takes virtually no time.

Using the Activity Sheets on pages 56 and 57

Several practical activities can help children to understand what is happening in the atmosphere.

Thunderstorms usually occur on a warm summer's day. Rapid movement of moist air causes a build up of static electricity (electricity held in one place). This is the type of electricity which the children will produce in the activities on pages 56 and 57. Electric charges build up on non-conducting materials − plastics and fabrics, for example − not on conductors, such as metals.

Normally, all objects have equal positive and negative charges. They are electrically neutral. When two different materials (non-metals) are rubbed together, weakly held negative charges (electrons) transfer from one material to the other, where they are more strongly held. One material gains electrons and becomes negatively charged, the other loses electrons and becomes positively charged.

Because electrically charged things want to return to their neutral state, there are strong attractive forces between opposite (+ and −) charges, and strong repulsive forces between like (+, + and −, −) charges.

The range of activities on pages 56 and 57 encourage children to experiment with static electricity.

1 A charge builds up on the balloon. The balloon is attracted to the opposite 'induced' charge on the wall. If the balloon is placed against earthed metal, the charge flows away, so the balloon does not 'stick' to the metal.

Dry non-conducting surfaces do not conduct electricity. On damp surfaces the electricity flows through the moisture.

2 The glass screen has a static charge on it due to the operation of the TV. Screens attract dust because of this charge.

3,4 The static electricity attracts small particles such as bits of paper and dust.

This phenomenon is used to filter (by attraction) dust and ash in power-station chimneys in order to reduce the pollutant concentration in the smoke.

The water will be bent (either attracted towards or repelled away) by the electric charge on the comb. Try a plastic ruler as an alternative.

5,6 If the two surfaces build up like charges by being rubbed, they will repel each other. If they have opposite charges, they will attract each other.

7 Hang different materials in the paper saddle. Test for attraction or repulsion.

8 Thunder is caused by the rapid heating of the air when lightning strikes. The air reaches a temperature of many thousand degrees Celsius. This heat causes the air to expand and move very quickly − faster than the speed of sound − causing the crash of thunder. Popping a paper or crisp bag simulates this effect. The air is forced to move at great speed through the gap in the bursting bag.

Safety
Discuss with the children safety measures during a thunderstorm.

Never stand under a tree.

When in the open, keep low or run for shelter.

You are safe in a car. The electricity will be carried to the ground through the outside of the car body.

MAKING ELECTRICAL CHARGES

1 You need

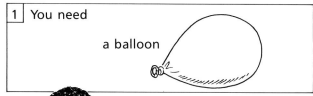

a balloon

Blow up the balloon.
Rub it on your jumper.

Find out to which
surfaces it will stick.

Record your findings.
Add surfaces of your own.

Surface	Sticks	Doesn't stick	Length of time it sticks
Wall			
door			
dry window			
wet window			
metal			

2 You need

TV

Computer

Switch on your computer.
Can you feel and hear
anything when you put your
hand near the screen?

	T.V.	Computer
Feel		
hear		

3 You need

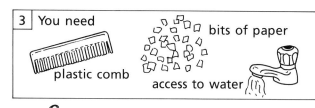

plastic comb

bits of paper

access to water

Comb your hair
with a plastic comb.

Try to pick up small pieces of paper by placing
the comb near to them.

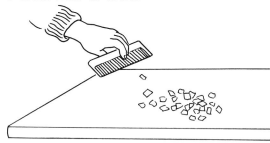

What happens?

Slowly move the comb near to the water. Don't
touch it. Comb your hair and try again.

What happens?

4 You need

plastic pen

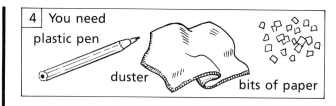

duster

bits of paper

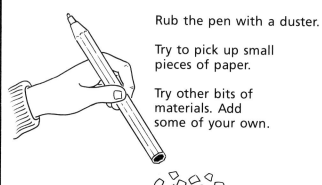

Rub the pen with a duster.

Try to pick up small
pieces of paper.

Try other bits of
materials. Add
some of your own.

Record the results.

Materials	What happens ?
plastic	
wood	
metal	
cornflakes	
cotton	

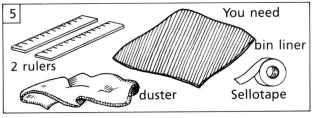

5
You need
2 rulers
bin liner
duster
Sellotape

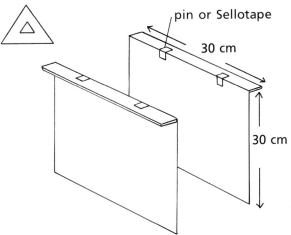

pin or Sellotape
30 cm
30 cm

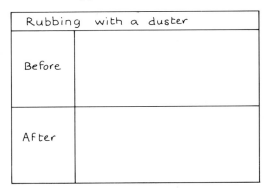

Cut out two pieces of polythene. Hang each from a separate ruler. Move the rulers together slowly.

Rub both inner surfaces with a duster.

Record what happens.

Rubbing with a duster	
Before	
After	

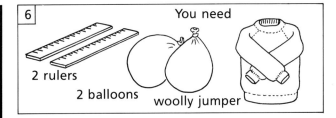

6
You need
2 rulers
2 balloons
woolly jumper

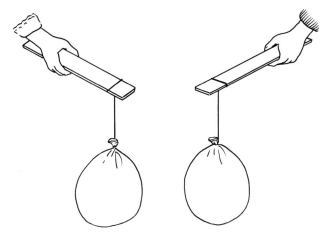

Slowly move the two balloons together.

Rub each balloon on your jumper. Slowly move them together.

Record what happens.

Rubbing on a woolly jumper	
Before	
After	

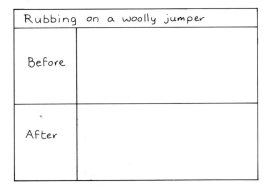

7
You need
2 plastic rulers
duster
paper saddle

Hang a plastic ruler in a paper saddle.

Slowly move another plastic ruler near to it.

Rub both rulers with a duster and repeat the experiment.

Record what happens.

Rubbing with a duster	
Before	
After	

8
paper bags
You need
Crisps
lots of puff

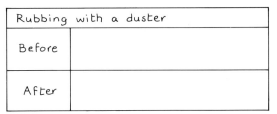

Discuss with a friend what happens.

PRESSURE AT WORK

1

card

air pressure

2

3

Orange Drink

4

5

straw

fishing line or string

balloon

bulldog clip

6

7

8

brick

9

A change in air pressure is the most important indicator of a change in the weather. This theme is considered globally on page 77.

Air pressure is measured using a barometer. The most popular type is the aneroid, which consists of a cylindrical metal box containing air at very low pressure. A steel spring prevents the box from collapsing. The top of the box is thin and flexible. Increasing air pressure pushes the top down. Under decreasing pressure, the top rises through the action of the spring. A lever arrangement is attached to the top and magnifies this small movement.

The change in air pressure is the predictor for future weather. Barometers have a small movable pointer to mark a reading so that a change from it may be spotted. Use the barometer with your weather recording. How good a predictor is it? Air pressure, measured in millibars (mb), can be read on the barometer and recorded.

Pressure measurements are taken in thousands of places throughout the world every few hours. From these, meteorologists are able to build up pressure maps, in which lines are drawn joining points of equal pressure. These are called isobars.

The Activity Sheet on page 58 encourages children to explore the effects of the pressure of the air around us (atmospheric pressure).

Activity 1 demonstrates that the air exerts a pressure and that this pressure is great. Carry out the task over a sink. Fill a beaker to overflowing and then slide a piece of card over its rim. Holding the card in place, invert the beaker and remove the support for the card. The card and water stay in place. The upward force resulting from the pressure of the air acts against the card: that is, against the weight of water supported by the card. Air pressure acts in every direction – up, down, left, right ...

The same principle is used in the sucker. The sucker is pushed against a flat surface, forcing out the air and leaving a partial vacuum (air at low pressure). The unbalanced air pressure on its outside holds the sucker to the surface. A damp surface helps to maintain an air-tight seal.

What makes a good sucker? Test a selection on various surfaces: glass, paper, card, wood, metal, rough, smooth, wet, dry ... Hang small weights (building blocks, for example) from the sucker to test its holding power.

Activity 2 shows how a higher than normal air pressure can be used for fun and work. The extra air pressure created by blowing down the paper tube forces it to unwind. As the air is expelled through the gap, it makes a noise. Air bags working on this principle may be a future life-saving feature in cars, inflating over the dashboard area of a car in an impact, so protecting the passengers.

Is the empty orange squash container (**Activity 3**) really empty? Connect a vacuum cleaner to the top of the plastic bottle. Wrap sticky tape round the neck to achieve an air-tight connection.

The cleaner motor drives a fan which blows the air from inside the cleaner to the outside, creating a space almost without air (partial vacuum). Air rushes up the cleaner attachments to fill this low-pressure space. (In normal operation, the air stream entrains dirt from the floor, which is caught in a paper or fabric bag.) What happens to the squash bottle? The air inside it is removed and so the internal air pressure drops. The much greater normal air pressure on the outside can easily push in the wall of the bottle, which is no longer balanced by the internal air pressure.

Activity 4 demonstrates that air surrounds us and occupies space. Use a small plastic drinks bottle. No water can enter the bottle until the air is allowed to escape. No water can leave the bottle until air can enter the bottle to fill the space which would be vacated by the water.

Activity 5 demonstrates that high-pressure air always escapes to a low-pressure area, and will do so with some force. A storm or a hurricane occurs when a large pressure difference develops and air rushes – with great force – from the high to the low-pressure area.

Activity 6 shows that air has mass. Use a maths balance, bulldog clips and two balloons. Adjust the positions of the balloons in a draught-free area to achieve a balance. Release the air from one balloon. The balloon containing the air is heavier and the balance will tip. One litre of air weighs about 1 gram. **Activity 7** attempts to measure this. Accurate, sensitive scales will be needed. Ask your local secondary school if you may borrow a scientific balance.

A home-made barometer features in **Activity 8**. The partly-filled plastic bottle is inverted in a water-filled tray. A brick supports the bottle and a ruler is stuck to its side. Mark or record the level of the water. When the air pressure increases, the water will be pushed up the bottle. When it decreases, the level will fall. Record your results and compare them with the classroom barometer and your other weather measurements.

Which way will the air flow to fill a low-pressure area? **Activity 9** uses water instead of air. Fill a sink full of water and allow it to settle. Carefully unplug the sink and watch the water rush to the lower-pressure area. The children could draw arrows on the circles to show that the water (and air) circulates in an anticlockwise direction (in the northern hemisphere).

Rain, hail and snow – precipitation – form part of the Rain or Water Cycle. About 75% of the earth is covered in water. The evaporation (liquid into vapour) and condensation (vapour to liquid) of this water creates clouds which may be blown over land. The driving energy is provided by the sun. Heat and wind cause evaporation from the seas, lakes, rivers and vegetation. Industry, animals and people also add to the water vapour in the air. As the vapour rises, it cools (the temperature falls, on average, by 0.6°C for each additional 100 m of altitude) to form minute droplets of water or ice crystals (depending on temperature). If the droplets are cooled further, they increase in size and fall as rain, hail or snow. Clouds cool when they are forced higher either by passing over high ground or by meeting colder air.

Rain may be polluted by waste gases, such as nitrogen oxides and sulphur dioxide, from vehicles and industry. The gases are dissolved by the vapour forming and may fall as acid rain many hundreds of kilometres from where it was formed, perhaps in another country. Acid rain seriously damages plants, water life and buildings.

The acid content of a liquid can be tested using Universal Indicator paper, which changes colour according to the level of acidity or alkalinity.

UNIVERSAL INDICATOR	ACID	NEUTRAL	ALKALI
	RED	GREEN	BLUE/PURPLE
PH VALUE	1	→ 7 ←	14

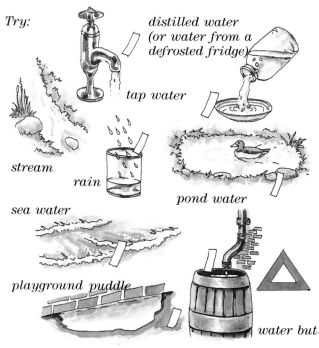

Try: distilled water (or water from a defrosted fridge)

tap water

stream

rain

pond water

sea water

playground puddle

water but

To see the effects of acid rain, put a piece of chalk in lemon juice. Test the juice with the Universal Indicator. The prevailing wind brings the chemical-laden rain, which drives into cracks in buildings and attacks the building materials. In winter, this also causes frost damage (page 27), breaking off pieces of stone or brick. Seeds carried by the wind also enter cracks and cause damage as they grow. Look around the school or local churchyard for evidence of this.

CONDENSATION

CONDENSATION

RAIN SHADOW

PREVAILING WIND

EVAPORATION

EVAPORATION

Rain may soak into the ground or stay on the surface. Then where does it go? Around the school, much of the surface water is directed into the ground-water drains and eventually finds its way to rivers or streams. But what happens to the water in the soil? Study types of soil drainage to find out. Try earthy soil, sand, clay, chalk. Dig a hole to discover your type of ground.

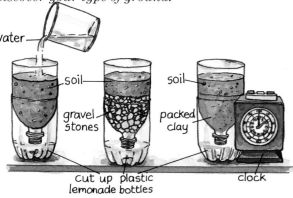

Which type drains best, fastest? If there is a solid layer of clay or impermeable rock, what will happen to the water?

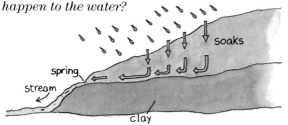

As the water flows back to the sea, it is used to supply our water needs and those of industry and farming.

Patterns of rain
Some areas of the British Isles receive more rain than others. The prevailing winds blow from the west and south-west, so western and south-western Britain receives moisture-bearing clouds first. These clouds release their moisture over hills and mountains, which are situated mainly in the west or centrally, leaving the lower land in the east with drier weather. See the maps on page 79.

Why is sea water salty?

On its return path from land to sea, the water has passed through soil and rock. It dissolves some of the minerals in the ground and these are carried to the sea. These amounts are very small, but over millions of years, the concentration of minerals (salts) in the seas and oceans has built up. Some seas are 'saltier' than others. Those which do not link with large oceans have become very salty. If the sea is salty, why doesn't rain taste salty?

The first stage of rain formation is evaporation. In the evaporation of a salt solution only pure water turns into vapour, leaving the salt behind.

- Make up a salt solution in a bottle.
- Add as much salt as will dissolve.
- If you use warm water, you will find that more salt will dissolve.
- Fill one saucer (A) with tap water, the other (B) with your salt solution and label them carefully.
- Leave them on a sunny window sill and keep saucer A topped up with tap water, saucer B with a salt solution. (This will ensure that the quantity of salt remaining after evaporation can be seen easily.)
- To make the tests fair, use the same amount of water for each saucer. When all the water has evaporated, study the saucers. The salt will have been left behind.

In areas of the world where the water-cycle brings insufficient water, other methods must be used. Seawater can produce fresh water by an industrial version of your saucer experiment, in which the evaporated water vapour is captured.

You will need:

length of plastic piping

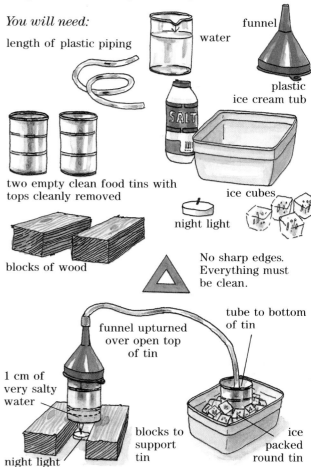

Taste the (very) salty water on the tip of your tongue. Light the night light to heat the water (simulating the sun as the energy source in the water-cycle). The vapour will travel along the tube, cool and condense (turn back into water) and be captured in the second can. Taste again. In industry, this process is called desalination.

Measuring wind speed

Two types of wind-measuring device are available from school equipment suppliers (see page 79): anemometer and ventimeter.

hand-held anemometer

ventimeter

Both measure wind speed. The scale on each may be given in miles per hour, kilometres per hour or metres per second. Readings should be taken at least twice. If there is a huge difference, more readings are needed. This search for validity should be discussed with the children.

The anemometer or ventimeter should be held in position for at least 15 seconds.

The ventimeter is not expensive and is cheaper and more robust than an anemometer for school use.

Make your own wind speed indicator

thick card or cardboard

mark card to count number of rotations

plastic pen top pushed through centre

knitting needle

washing-up liquid bottle

4 yoghurt cartons pushed along slits

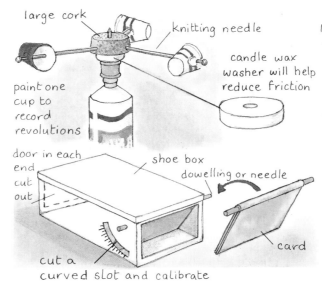

large cork

knitting needle

candle wax washer will help reduce friction

paint one cup to record revolutions

door in each end cut out

shoe box

dowelling or needle

card

cut a curved slot and calibrate

As the wind blows, the card flap will be blown upwards. The stronger the wind, the higher the flap will lift. The scale on the slot side can be numbered to indicate the wind speed.

Using your wind speed indicator

The scale on the side of your box or the number of rotations in 10 seconds can be related to an accurate measure (calibration). Use your school-made device alongside a ventimeter or anemometer and compare readings. Fairly accurate markings may be made on the side of the shoe-box wind measurer. For rotating machines, the children may build up a record of comparisons and draw a conversion graph similar to those on page 64.

Number of turns in 10 seconds	Measured wind speed

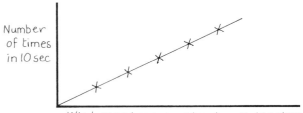

Number of times in 10 sec

Wind speed measured using ventimeter

The Beaufort Scale was developed by Admiral Sir Francis Beaufort in 1806 as a method of grouping wind speeds and their effects.

Use your wind-speed indicator, ventimeter or estimate the speed by observation. Keep a daily record.

Day	Wind Speed		
	Estimated	Measured	Beaufort
Monday	10 kph	8 kph	2

The Beaufort Scale is given on page 64. Currently, weather reports give wind speed in miles per hour. The graphs (page 64) will allow the children to convert from one scale to another. The Beaufort Scale goes from Calm (Force 0) to Hurricane (Force 12). Everyday experience of your pupils will be Force 0-4. National or international reports will provide opportunities to use the higher values.

Electricity from wind

The anemometer can be connected to a Lego motor. The wires from the motor are connected to a meter. The faster the motor is turned, the more electricity is produced (see page 79).

Using the windrose

The windrose can be used with different age groups in different ways. The reading is of wind direction. Key Stage 2 children should use eight compass points. Prevailing wind patterns will soon emerge in the readings. The record of wet winds leads to a discussion of why some winds carry moisture.

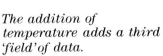

From which direction? Have the winds crossed sea or land on their way to you? Are westerlies often wet, easterlies dry?

The addition of temperature adds a third 'field' of data.

What is the correlation between direction and temperature? Which land or sea have the winds crossed?

Remember: continental Europe can be very hot in summer and bitterly cold in winter. Seasonal differences are very marked and should be compared and discussed.

Exchanging wind data with other schools is easy and helps build up regional patterns.
Note: schools in valleys or on coasts may find strong local variations to the regional pattern.

Evidence of wind

Where are the windiest parts of the playground? The children may develop earlier experiences (pages 9 and 10).

Where should we measure the wind?

The 'official' method of measuring wind direction and speed is to carry out the measurement at a height of 10 metres above clear, level ground. The difference in speed and direction at this height and at 1 metre (hand-held) above ground level is quite small. Compare the direction of the wind at your level with the direction of the clouds. Clouds at different heights may move in different directions and at different speeds.

Can you see evidence of prevailing winds in your locality? Over a period of time the trees may grow 'bent'.

Look for evidence of wind direction in your surroundings. The effects of rain or snow may give you a clue.

Can you design your own wind speed/direction machine? Here are some more ideas.

Hold the protractor level. Read off the angle and compare the result with a measured or estimated (Beaufort) speed.

Modify a clinometer.

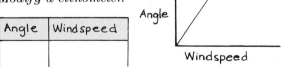

Angle	Windspeed

THE BEAUFORT SCALE

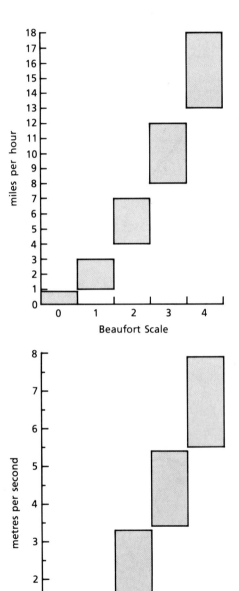

Wind Speed Range (10m above ground)		Force	Beaufort Scale Description	What Happens	
metres per sec	miles per hour				
0.0-0.2	0-0.9	0	calm	Smoke rises straight up.	
0.3-1.5	1-3	1	light air	Smoke drifts. Wind vane does not turn.	
1.6-3.3	4-7	2	light breeze	Wind felt on face. Leaves rustle. Wind vanes move.	
3.4-5.4	8-12	3	gentle breeze	Leaves and small twigs move all the time. Flags flutter.	
5.5-7.9	13-18	4	moderate breeze	Dust and paper blow about. Small branches move.	
8.0-10.7	19-24	5	fresh breeze	Small trees begin to sway.	
10.8-13.8	25-31	6	strong breeze	Large branches move. Telephone wires whistle. Umbrellas difficult to hold.	
13.9-17.1	32-38	7	near gale	Difficult to walk against the wind. Whole trees move.	
17.2-20.7	39-46	8	gale	Twigs broken from trees.	
20.8-24.4	47-54	9	strong gale	Damage to houses - slates and chimney pots blown off.	
24.5-28.4	55-63	10	storm	Trees uprooted. Considerable damage to buildings.	

RECORDING DIRECTION

Name/Group:

_____

Dates From: _____

To: _____

Instructions

Record the wind speed and direction daily.

If the day is 'dry', colour the rectangle **red**.

If the day is 'wet', colour the rectangle **blue**.

Write the wind speed in the rectangle.

N

NW

NE

W

E

SW

SE

S

Predicting the weather is not easy. Even with the aid of some of the world's most powerful computers, weather forecasters expect only an 80% success rate. One reason for this lack of certainty is the great number of variables involved in weather prediction.

Therefore, we should not expect children to achieve a high success rate in weather prediction, but we should be able to help them to develop these skills:

- Observe and discern patterns
- Recognise causal relationships
- Use units of measurement and ranges
- Use proportionality – direct and inverse
- Recognise anomalies
- Data handling
- Organisation
- Fair testing
- Estimation
- Prediction

The chart on page 67 enables the children to collect a range of data in one place. If you choose not to collect data from one or more of the categories, then simply leave the row blank.

As more data is added each day, the children should try to estimate the next day's likely readings. These estimations should be based on their experience of patterns seen earlier in the recording process. This will not be easy at first. The children will not have sufficient information and will lack experience. As both increase, however, we will see a marked development from 'guesswork' to 'estimation'.

The children should try to discover whether one particular aspect of the weather is a more reliable predictor than others. Look for evidence of success in one or more aspects of their forecasting, such as 'rain' or 'dry'.

A careful study of the data will show patterns developing. This is often easier to recognise when depicted graphically rather than as columns of numbers.

The information collected on page 67 is easily transferred into a computer database.

Wind-chill factor

The build-up of excess heat in the human body is controlled by sweating and the dilation of the blood capillaries close to the skin. Hence the red faces after an energetic run or sports session.

The wind, particularly during dry weather, continuously removes the evaporating sweat and so cools the skin. This cooling effect lowers the perceived temperature – that is, it 'feels' colder than it actually is. This is especially so in cold weather: a 'biting wind' is most unpleasant, in sharp contrast to the desirable 'cool breeze' in summer.

There is growing awareness of the importance of the wind-chill factor in determining people's well-being. Temperature readings are insufficient indicators of how people will actually feel and respond to the weather.

The wind-chill table below compares the actual measured temperature with the perceived (felt) temperature.

Wind Speed metres/sec / Temperature °C	0	2.5	5	7.5	10	15	20
				Chill	▶		
	10	8.7	6.4	4.4	2.7	0.2	−1.4
	8	6.7	4.2	2.0	0.2	−2.5	−4.2
	6	4.6	2.0	−0.4	−2.3	−5.2	−7.0
	4	2.5	−0.3	−2.8	−4.8	−7.9	−10.0
	2	0.4	−2.5	−5.2	−7.3	−10.7	−12.9
	0	−1.2	−4.8	−7.5	−9.9	−13.3	−15.8
	−2	−3.7	−7.1	−9.9	−12.3	−16.1	−18.6
	−4	−5.8	−9.3	−12.3	−14.8	−18.8	−21.4
	−6	−7.9	−11.6	−14.6	−17.3	−21.3	−24.2
	−8	−10.0	−13.9	−17.0	−19.9	−24.0	−27.0
	−10	−12.1	−16.1	−19.4	−22.4	−26.6	−29.8

The Activity Sheet on page 68 is a useful exercise in reading and responding to data from around the world. Similar activities can be developed by using the data in a good reference atlas.

Questions about 'calendars', such as farming calendars in different parts of the world, help children to appreciate that the weather systems in the British Isles are not typical of weather systems elsewhere and that the seasons in some latitudes do not correspond to 'our' seasons.

Day	1	2	3	4	5	6	7	8	9	10	11	12	13	14	15
Wind direction															
Wind speed															
Temperature															
Rain															
Humidity															
Pressure															

Day	16	17	18	19	20	21	22	23	24	25	26	27	28	29	30	31
Wind direction																
Wind speed																
Temperature																
Rain																
Humidity																
Pressure																

COMPARING WEATHER

The first three graphs show the average monthly rainfall in each of the three capital cities.

We add the rainfall for each month in order to find the Annual Rainfall Total.

Use a calculator to find the Annual Rainfall Totals for:

a) London _____ mm
b) Moscow _____ mm
c) Athens _____ mm

Which city has the highest rainfall?

_____

Which city has the lowest rainfall?

_____

Which is the wettest month in:

a) London _____
b) Moscow _____
c) Athens _____

Which is the driest month in:

a) London _____
b) Moscow _____
c) Athens _____

Which is the wettest city in November?

_____

Which is the driest city in December?

_____

London receives rain all year round.

Athens has most of its rain in summer/winter

Moscow has most of its rain in summer/winter

Put a tick ✓ over your answer.

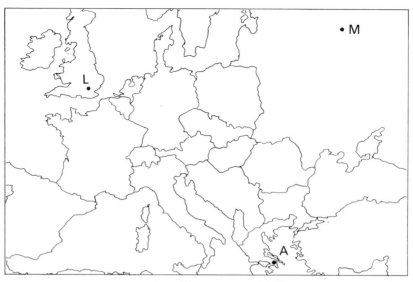

RAINFALL

LONDON

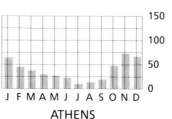

MOSCOW

ATHENS

The average highest temperature in London is 17°C.

The average lowest temperature in London is 4°C.

The difference between the highest and the lowest temperatures is known as the Annual Range. In London it is 13°C.

Highest average in Moscow _____ °C

Lowest average in Moscow _____ °C

Range in Moscow _____ °C

Highest average in Athens _____ °C

Lowest average in Athens _____ °C

Range in Athens _____ °C

Which city has the largest range? _____

Which city has the smallest range? _____

Which city is the warmest in

a) July _____ b) January _____

Which city is the coldest in

a) July _____ b) January _____

TEMPERATURE

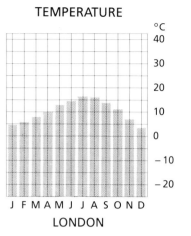

LONDON

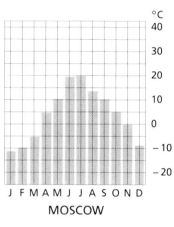

MOSCOW

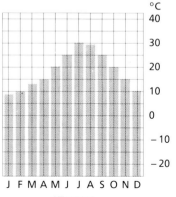

ATHENS

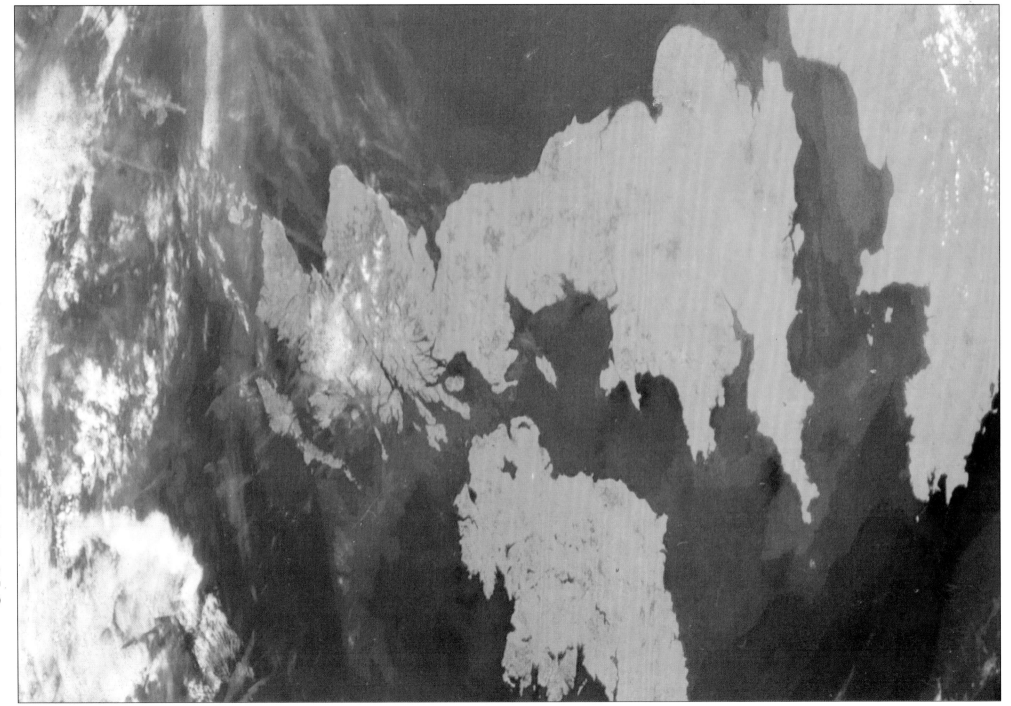

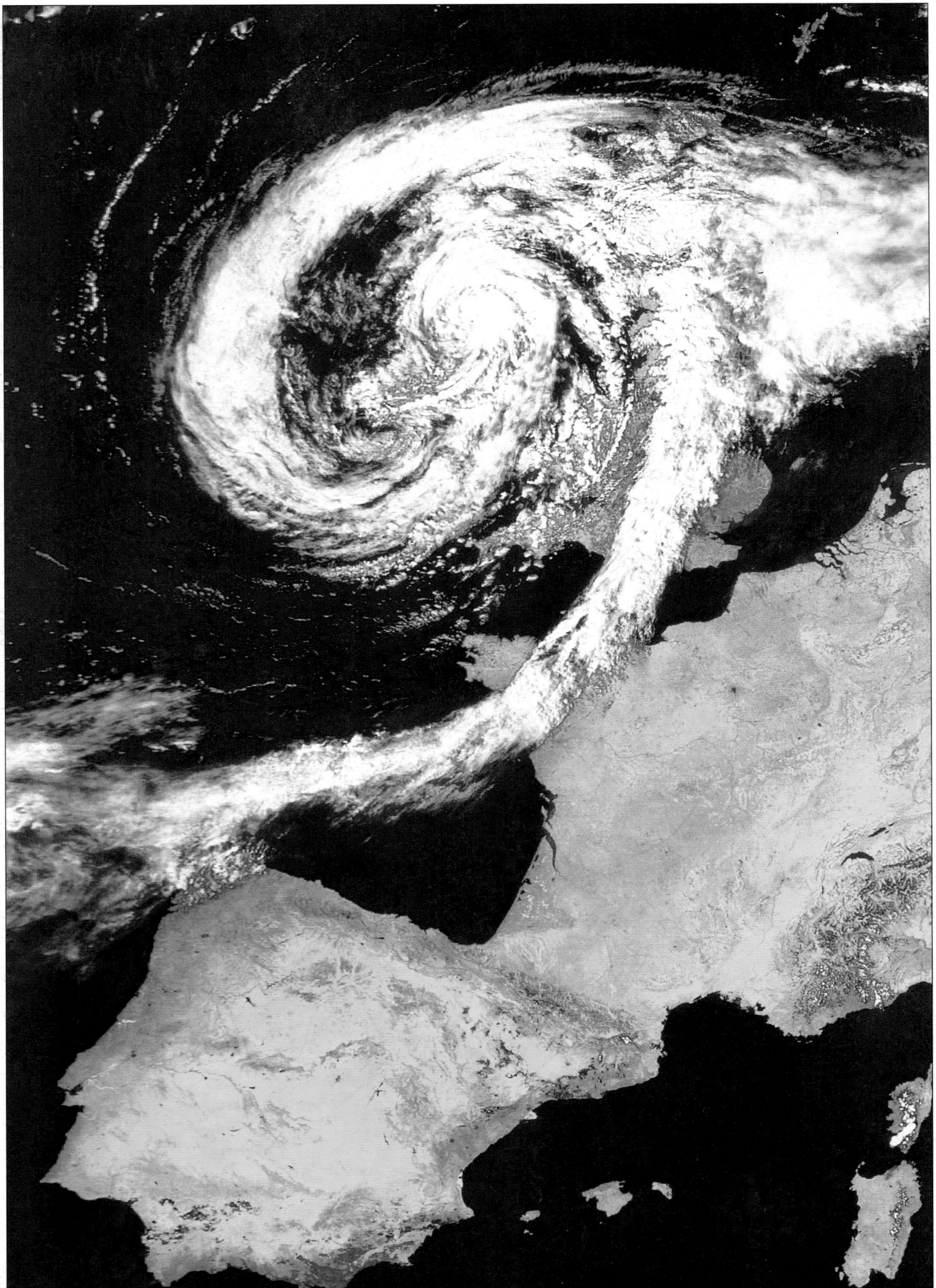

SATELLITE PICTURE OF UK

EIU is one of the National Curriculum's cross-curricular themes which needs to be planned for when designing curriculum policy statements, schemes of work and small units of work in the form of topics. Some subjects and topics have more potential than others for developing EIU. Weather is one of them. Pages 73-76 explore aspects of everyday life which are affected by the weather and have considerable potential for developing EIU.

The activity on page 73 links weather conditions to hospital cases. Teacher-led discussion can develop the idea of costs: to the individual in personal suffering and loss of earnings; to companies in the loss of trained staff and transport equipment; to insurance companies in claims and their policy holders in premiums; to

tax-payers funding health care. A study of the reports in local newspapers following a cold spell or a gale will reveal increases in weather-related cases.

Weather has a direct effect on energy consumption, which is explored on page 74. Children may well think of domestic uses of power but should also be encouraged to consider demand from industry. It is not just temperature but also light levels (and therefore seasons) which affect demand. Children can be given the opportunity to predict the consumption of electricity in school and to monitor actual use.

The activity on pages 75 and 76 involves role-play and a decision-making exercise. It concerns the old dilemma of services against costs. The

activity may be extended by allocating the costs of salt, vehicle and wages to the exercise. Some local authorities will supply unit costs: for example £X per km.

In addition to the Activity Sheets provided in this book, there are countless other opportunities to consider weather and its links to EIU in the wider curriculum. Some possibilities are proposed here.

History

Geography

Science and technology

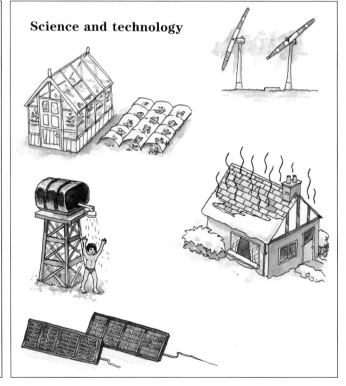

POWER TO THE PEOPLE

The amount of electricity used by a piece of electrical equipment is measured in watts (W) or kilowatts (kW).

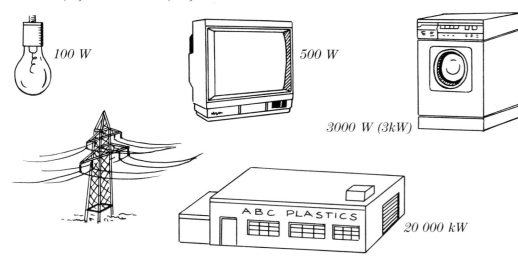

100 W

500 W

3000 W (3kW)

20 000 kW

To supply the whole of a country with electricity, the generating companies make electricity by the millions of watts (megawatts – MW). The graph below shows the electricity demand in Britain for a typical working day in winter.

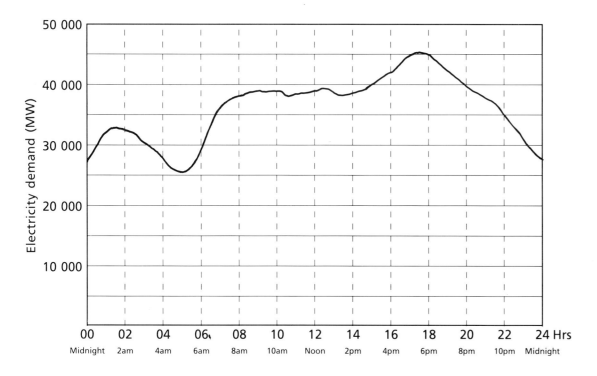

1 *Use the graph to find out:*
● *The time at which the demand for electricity is highest.*

_____

● *The time at which the demand for electricity is lowest.*

_____

2 *Why do you think the demand is (a) highest and (b) lowest at these times?*

a) _____

b) _____

● *If the maximum amount of electricity available from the generating companies is 54 000 MW, how much electricity is not being used at 17:00 (5 pm)?*

_____

3 *What do you think most of the electricity will be used for between 09:00 (9 am) and 17:00 (5 pm)?*

_____

4 *On a separate piece of paper, make a list of the ways we use electricity: at home, at school, in shops and in factories. Think carefully about the effects of the weather on the use of electricity.*

Location	On a dark, wet, cold winter's day, we use electricity for:	On a dry, hot and sunny summer's day we use electricity for:
At home		

5 *At what time on Christmas Day do you think the demand for electricity is highest? Explain your answer.*

_____

6 *Will the pattern for electricity demand in summer be the same as that shown in the winter graph? Think about: hours of daylight, temperature, eating habits ....*

_____

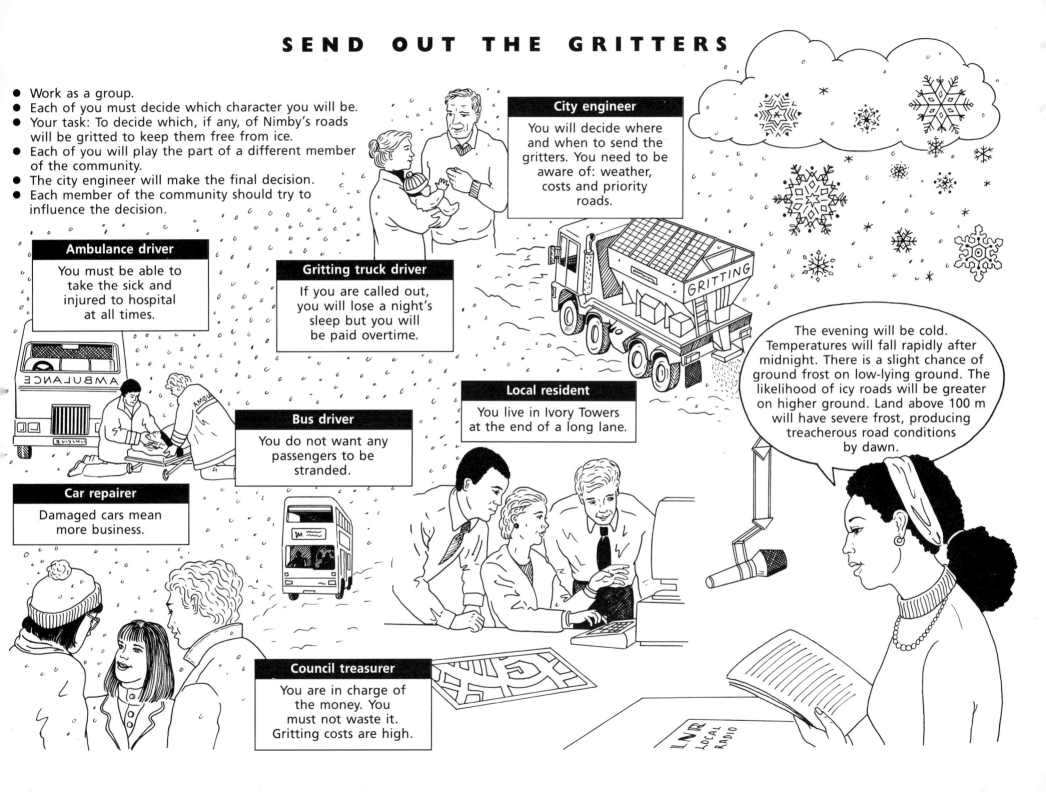

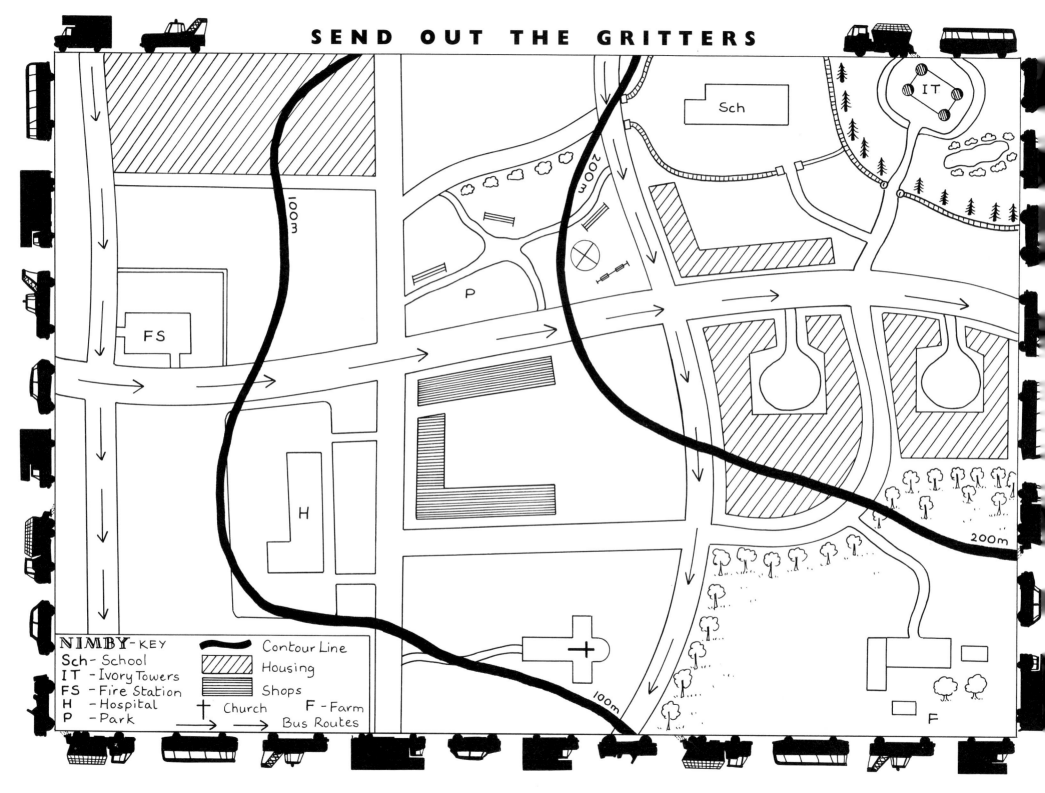

SEND OUT THE GRITTERS

Sch

IT

100m

200m

Sch

P

FS

H

200m

100m

F

NIMBY -KEY
Sch - School
IT - Ivory Towers
FS - Fire Station
H - Hospital
P - Park

Contour Line
Housing
Shops
✝ Church
F - Farm
Bus Routes

Climate is average weather. In Britain, the climate is temperate, summers are warm and winters mild. The changeability of Britain's weather is a major feature. Other climates children should discuss are rain forest (hot and rainy), desert (dry with little difference between summer and winter) and polar.

Areas with tropical climates can have extremes of very dry and very wet periods. Being close to the equator, such areas have high average temperatures. Humid conditions are common, as are tropical storms, typhoons, cyclones and hurricanes. These build up around areas of very low air pressure over the sea and produce winds of up to 200 km/h, causing widespread loss of life and damage to crops and property.

'Highs' and 'lows'

Air pressure does not remain constant. Due to the heating effect of the sun on the ground, air gets warm, expands and rises, being replaced by cooler, denser air. This, coupled with the rotation of the earth, creates areas of higher and lower-than-average (normal) pressure. These 'highs' and 'lows' try to balance out their differences, the air from a high-pressure area rushing to fill a low-pressure area. This movement of air is the 'wind'. The greater the difference in pressure, the greater the force and speed of the wind. Due to the rotation of the earth, the air in the northern hemisphere circulates anticlockwise around a low-pressure area (a depression) and clockwise around a high-pressure area (an anticyclone). In the southern hemisphere, the reverse obtains.

rotation of earth

equator

air rushing in to fill a low

If we can measure the change of air pressure, we should be able to predict the weather. High pressure in the British Isles will bring hot, dry, sunny weather in summer because, with a 'high'

over the land, air flows from land to sea, therefore few clouds are present and the sky is clear. In winter, clear skies produce very cold nights because there will be no clouds to blanket the earth and the ground will quickly give up its heat. Low pressure will cause air to rush towards the centre of the 'low'. This airflow will pass over the sea, bringing clouds and rain.

Variety

Are all temperate climates the same? Both London and Moscow have temperate climates, yet their weather patterns are quite different (see page 68). This is because the British Isles has a 'maritime' climate, in which the sea evens out seasonal temperature differences, whereas Moscow has a 'continental' climate reflected in large swings in seasonal temperature. The climate of different countries may be investigated. Groups could 'adopt' a city and record the weather over a period of time.

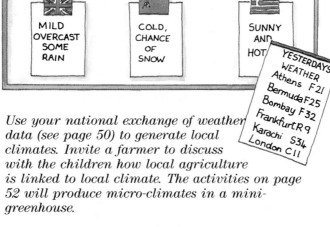

MILD OVERCAST SOME RAIN

COLD, CHANCE OF SNOW

SUNNY AND HOT

YESTERDAYS WEATHER
Athens F21
Bermuda F25
Bombay F32
Frankfurt R9
Karachi S34
London C11

Use your national exchange of weather data (see page 50) to generate local climates. Invite a farmer to discuss with the children how local agriculture is linked to local climate. The activities on page 52 will produce micro-climates in a mini-greenhouse.

Climate and weathering

Types of weathering are related to climate. Periods of rain and frost will fracture rock. Water which penetrates small crevices will expand on freezing (see page 27) with enormous

force, breaking off sizeable sections. Wind-blown seeds may find their way into small openings on buildings or rockfaces. As they grow, their root systems can fracture the surrounding material. The chemicals carried by the rain, however, can damage structural materials (see page 60).

The global climate

The 'greenhouse effect' is caused by the build up of carbon dioxide gas in the atmosphere.

> In a greenhouse, the short-wave radiation from the sun can pass through glass. This radiation is absorbed by the contents of the greenhouse, which get warmer and emit their own long-wave radiation which cannot penetrate glass. Much of this radiation is re-radiated back into the greenhouse and the temperature builds up.

Among the main sources of carbon dioxide are vehicle engines and coal and oil-burning industries. Carbon dioxide is removed from the atmosphere by plants – particularly trees – which convert it to oxygen as part of their food chain. So, as more forests are cut down, less carbon dioxide is removed. A rise of only a few degrees in the temperature of the global climate would further melt the polar ice caps and cause changes in regional climates.

The Ozone Layer is part of the earth's upper atmosphere. It absorbs harmful rays from the sun. Holes in this layer have been detected over Antarctica, the cause of which is believed to be the build up of chlorofluorocarbons (CFCs) in the upper atmosphere. CFCs are used in aerosols, refrigerators and throwaway food packaging. If the screening effect of this layer is reduced, average temperatures will increase, melting the ice caps. Low-lying areas could be flooded.

GEOGRAPHY

AT	Statement of Attainment	Page
1/2d	Record weather observations made over a short period.	9, 10, 12, 15, 17, 19, 21-23, 27, 33, 37-39, 46, 48-51, 53, 59, 62, 63, 65-67, 69
1/4d	Measure and record weather using direct observation and simple equipment.	5, 8-12, 15, 17, 19, 21, 23, 27, 33, 37-40, 46, 48-53, 59-63, 65, 67
1/5d	Extract information from thematic maps which show distribution patterns.	47, 49, 50, 68, 69, 79
1/6e	Measure and record weather using scientific instruments and procedures.	12, 15, 17, 19, 21-23, 27, 33, 37, 38, 40, 46-49, 50-53, 59, 61-63, 65-67
2/4e	Describe how the daily life of a locality in an economically developing country is affected by its landscape, weather and wealth.	16, 17, 30, 51, 60-62, 72
3/2a	Recognise seasonal weather patterns.	15, 20, 21, 23, 27, 28, 30, 33, 34, 37, 38, 40, 46-50, 63, 65-68, 72-76, 79
3/2b	Identify the forms in which water occurs in the environment.	14-16, 18-21, 26-30, 38-40, 51-55, 60, 61, 70, 72, 73 75-77
3/3a	Describe contrasting weather conditions in parts of the world.	16, 17, 26, 28, 30, 33, 47, 50, 51, 60-63, 68, 72
3/3b	Describe what happens to rainwater when it reaches the ground.	14-16, 18, 19, 21, 26-28, 51, 52, 60, 61, 72, 73, 75, 76
3/4a	Explain how site conditions can influence surface temperatures and local wind speed and direction.	13, 18, 22, 28, 62-65, 68-76, 77, 79
3/5a	Describe differences in the mean seasonal distribution of temperatures and rainfall over the British Isles.	40, 50, 61, 65-67, 69, 79
3/5b	Distinguish between weather and climate.	40, 47, 50, 61, 66-68, 77, 79
3/5d	Give evidence of different types of weathering and distinguish between weathering and erosion.	60, 61
3/6a	Explain that rainfall is caused by air rising and cooling, and relate the uplift of air to relief, convection and fronts.	38, 39, 50, 55, 60, 61, 65, 70, 71, 77, 79

SCIENCE

AT	Statement of Attainment	Page
3/1a	Know that there are daily and seasonal changes in the weather.	Throughout the book
3/1b	Be able to describe the apparent motion of the Sun across the sky.	21, 38
3/2a	Be able to record the weather over a period of time.	Throughout the book
3/2c	Understand the meaning of hot and cold.	20-37, 40, 46-51, 60, 61, 64, 66, 67, 72-77
3/3a	Understand from direct observations some of the effects of weathering on buildings or on the landscape.	17, 60
3/5a	Be able to describe the water cycle.	50, 52, 60, 61, 71
3/6a	Understand how different airstreams give different weather related to their recent path over land and sea.	70, 71, 77, 79
3/7a	Understand how the water cycle and some weather phenomena are driven by heat transfer processes such as convection and radiation.	77
4/1a	Be able to identify familiar and unfamiliar objects in terms of simple properties.	15,18
4/2b	Know that heating and cooling everyday materials can cause them to melt or solidify or change permanently.	15, 18, 60, 21, 26, 27, 61
4/5a	Be able to classify aqueous solutions as acidic, alkaline or neutral using pH.	60
5/1a	Understand that things can be moved by pushing or pulling them.	4-13
5/1d	Know about the simple properties of sound and light, including loud/soft, bright/dark, high/low notes and colours.	16
5/2a	Understand that pushes, pulls and squeezes can make things start moving, speed up, swerve, stop or change shape.	4-13, 58, 59
5/2b	Know that some materials conduct electricity while others do not.	55-57
5/2c	Know that light passes through some materials and not others and that when it does not shadows are formed.	38
5/3a	Know about the factors which cause objects to float or sink in water.	26
5/4a	Understand that the changes in movement of an object depend on the size and direction of the forces acting on it.	4-13, 58, 59, 62-65, 77
5/4c	Know that sound travels at a different speed from light.	55
5/5a	Understand the quantitative relationship between speed, distance and time.	55, 62-64
5/6a	Understand the relationship between an applied force, the area over which it acts and the resulting pressure.	58, 59

Note: For science, the 1991 proposed Attainment Targets (NATs) are cited.

Services to schools

Meteorological Office
Marketing Services
London Road
Bracknell RG12 2SZ
    Excellent service

Royal Meteorological Society
104 Oxford Road
Reading RG1 7LJ
    Teaching aids, wall charts,
    journals and books

Computer software

National Centre for
Educational Technology
Sir William Lyons Road
Science Park
University of Warwick
Coventry CV4 7EZ
    OURFACTS and Resource
    Weather programs

Newman Software
Newman College
Bartley Green
Birmingham B32 3NT
    Caxton wordprocessing program

Specialist equipment suppliers

A&L Scientific
14a Progress Industrial Park
Orders Lane
Kirkham PR4 2TZ
    Wide range of science and
    weather equipment at keen
    prices and with good service

Advisory Unit for Microtechnology
in Education
Endymion Road
Hatfield AL10 8AU
    Weather monitoring equipment

Campus 2000
Priory House
St John's Lane
London EC1M 4BX

ELTEC
Unit 57-59
Campus Road
Listerhills Science Park
Bradford BD7 1HR
    Concept Keyboard

Griffin & George
Bishop Meadow Road
Loughborough LE11 ORG
    Science equipment

Morley Electronics
Morley House
West Chirton
North Shields NE29 7TY
    Teletext decoder

Osmiroid International
Fareham Road
Gosport PO13 OAL
    Science equipment

Philip & Tacey
Northway
Andover SP10 5BA
    Science equipment

Philip Harris
Lynn Lane
Shenstone
Lichfield WS14 0EE
    Science equipment

Unilab Ltd
The Science Park
Hutton Street
Blackburn BB1 3BT
    Weather satellite receiver
    and science equipment

Distribution patterns for rainfall and temperature over the British Isles.
Select appropriate data from the sources below and use it on the blank master map (page 69). Match data to ability levels.

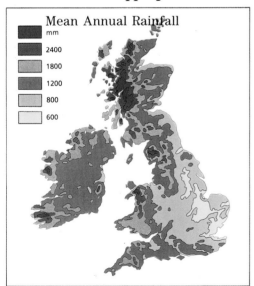

Note the marked east – west difference.

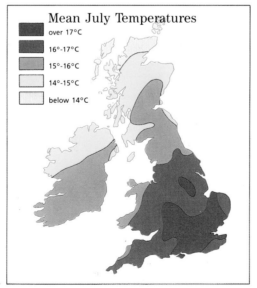

Note the marked north – south difference.

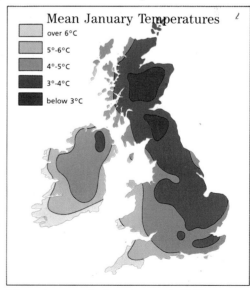

Note the marked east – west difference.

A

absorption
of heat 23
of moisture 54
accidents 72, 73
see also safety
acidity 60
air pressure
activities 58, 59
in weather forecasting 59, 77
see also anticyclones, barometers,
depressions
anemometers 62
anticyclones 77
Athens data 68

B

barometers 58, 59
bird scarers 8
burst pipes 27

C

Campus 2000 50
carbon dioxide 77
catgut in humidity meter 52, 53
Ceefax 47
charts
rainfall 19
temperature 21
weather/clothes 37
see also tables and records
climates 77
and clothes 23
clothes 17, 33, 36, 37
heat absorption 23, 24
heat reflection 23
waterproof 17
see also footwear
clouds
cover 21, 39
direction and speed 63
formation 60
types 38, 39
cobalt chloride 51, 52, 54
collages 17
compass points 9, 10, 46, 63
Concept Keyboard 48, 49
condensation 52, 60
cones as predictors 15
cooling 23, 25, 26, 60
costs 72
costumes 15

D

dance
rain 15
wind 4
databases 33, 46, 50, 66
dehumidifiers 52
depressions 77
satellite photograph 71
desalination 61
dew 51

E

drainage 18
soil tests 61
drama
rain 15
wind 4
draught excluders 5
draughts 5
drawing and painting
fan design 7
Noah's ark frieze 16
wind effects 4
drying 8, 51
see also evaporation

E

electrical charges
making 56, 57
in thunderstorms 55
electricity consumption 74
estimation 66
temperature 22, 27, 29
wind speed 12
evaporation 8, 18
and humidity 51
from salt solution 61
from skin 66
in water cycle 60

F

fair tests
drying 8
evaporation 18, 61
melting snow 15
rainfall 19
thermal insulation 23
fan making 7
fax links 50
flooding 16, 77
fog 51
folklore 41
footwear 17, 34
polishing shoes 17
forecasting 21, 41
accuracy 33, 42, 46, 66
and folklore 41, 42
freezing 26, 27
see also ice
frost 51
damage 60, 77

G

greenhouse effect 77
gritting 21, 26, 75, 76

H

hailstones 15
hair in humidity meter 52
hibernation 23
high-pressure areas 59, 77
history 43, 72
humidity 15, 51
measurement 51, 52, 53
and plant growth 52
hygrometers 51

I

ice 26
as hazard 21
melting 21, 26
on walkways and roads 21, 26, 75, 76
icebergs 26
information technology 46-50
isobars 59

L

language 41-45
leaf distribution 9, 10
lightning 55
London data 68, 77

M

melting *see* ice
mime 4
mobile making 4
Moscow data 68, 77
music
rain 15, 16
wind 4
mythology 6, 7, 43

N

newsheets 47
Noah 16

O

Odysseus 6, 7
oktas 38
Oracle 47
OURFACTS program 46
ozone layer 77

P

photographs
of wind effects 63
from satellites 49, 70, 71
picture matching 7
poems and rhymes 4, 16, 18, 41, 42,
43, 44, 45
pollution effects 60
pressure *see* air pressure
PROMPT program 49

R

rain
acid rain 60, 61
effects 14, 16
formation 60, 61
in poetry 43, 44
signs of 15
see also water cycle
rainbows 16
rain collector 19
rainfall
average monthly 68
distribution 79
measurement 19
patterns 61

rainwear 17
recording 33, 66
fax link in schools 50
see also charts, tables and records
reflection of heat 23
roofs 17

S

safety
in activities 17, 22, 23, 27, 38, 51,
54, 63
in cold weather 21
in thunderstorms 56
salt
effect on freezing 21, 26
as solute 54, 61
salt solutions
in de-icing 26
evaporation 54, 61
moisture absorption 54
sand play 16
satellite pictures 49, 50, 70, 71
scarecrows 8
school links
data exchange 63, 77
faxing weather records 50
local services 42
sea water 61
seasonal patterns 23, 38
seaweed as predictor 15, 52
seeds in wind 8, 60
shadow lengths 38
silica gel 52
snow 18
change to water 15
snowflakes 15
solar power 38
sucker action 59
summer 20, 28, 77
in poetry 45
sunshine 38
symbols 33, 35

T

tables and records
Beaufort scale 64
bird visits 8
clothes 17, 23
cloud cover 21, 37
electrical charge 56, 57
electricity consumption 74
leaf distribution 9, 10
melting ice 26
rain forecasts 15
rainfall 19
temperature 21, 22, 23, 24, 25, 26
various data 33, 46, 67
weekly weather 40
wind-chill factor 66
wind speed 12, 62, 63
Teletext 47

temperature 31, 32
annual range 68
changes 21
conversion 32
distribution 79
prediction 21
in wind 66
and wind direction 63
temperature measurement 23, 27
by feeling 22, 23
maximum/minimum 21
in school 22
in shade 22
in sun 22
see also thermometers
thermal insulation 26
tests, 23, 24, 25
thermometers 27
maximum/minimum 21
wet-and-dry 51
thunder 55
simulation 57

U

Universal Indicator 60

V

ventimeters 62
vocabulary development 43
cloze procedure 49

W

water cycle 60
water supply 16, 61
waterproof tests 17
waterproofing 17
weather services 46, 47
fax link in schools 50
school 'broadcasts' 33, 47
see also satellite pictures
weathering 60, 77
wind 77
from blowers 7
controlling 7
drying in 8, 51
effects 4, 5, 13, 63
prevailing 60, 63
sensing 4, 9
wind-chill factor 66
wind direction 9, 10, 63, 65
speed of rotation 12
template 11
wind roses 63, 65
wind speed
classification 12
Beaufort scale 64
measurement 12, 62, 63
see also anemometers, ventimeters
wind vanes 9
windmills 9
winter 20, 21, 28, 77
in poetry 44, 45
WRITER program 49